BRONZE
&
BEYOND

BRONZE
&
BEYOND

A glider pilot's guide

John McCullagh

Edition 12

First edition published in November 2004
Twelfth edition published in January 2012 by John McCullagh
39 The Farthings
KINGSTON-UPON-THAMES
KT2 7PT

ISBN 0-9548742-0-X

Cover photograph courtesy of whiteplanes.com

Cover artwork by john.w.saunders@btinternet.com

The part of the UK Airspace Classification and portions of the half million scale aeronautical chart for Southern England are reproduced with the kind permission of the Civil Aviation Authority.

Printed in the United Kingdom by Printondemand-worldwide.com Peterborough, UK. Set in 11 pt Garamond

CONTENTS

PREFACE TO FIRST EDITION

There are many books for glider pilots about how to fly, meteorology and aerodynamics. However, unlike the books for power pilots, none of the current books for glider pilots seems to cover everything that a British cross-country pilot should know. This book is an attempt to fill the gap.

The aim has been to be as brief as possible so that essential information is not lost in excessive detail. As a result, many of the things that a competent solo pilot should know already have been excluded. The test for inclusion for the remaining material has been "would they be better or safer pilots if they knew this?" Consequently some topics, especially meteorology and aerodynamics, have been pared down considerably compared to other books, though some background has to be given.

Many people will want to know more about some subjects and so a list of the books that are available for further reading has been provided. In particular The British Gliding Association publishes a booklet on air law as it affects glider pilots and on its operational regulations, *Laws and Rules for Glider Pilots*. Although the *Laws and Rules* have been quoted in a few places, this book does not attempt to replace it. You must also read the BGA's *Laws and Rules* in addition to this book.

This book is not a substitute for practical instruction in cross-country flying. In particular, dual flights with qualified instructors are essential to learn about flying cross-country and about landing in fields. You should also listen to as many experts as you can, and you should read other books and *Sailplane & Gliding*. These will all reinforce and supplement what has been covered in this book. You must also be fully briefed in advance of your first cross-country flights to ensure that you are aware of the conditions and the airspace restrictions that apply at the time.

Because this book has been aimed only at British pilots, it has a more limited market than other books on gliding. The economics of printing mean that a long period may elapse before an update can be issued. A web page, http://www.mccullagh.demon.co.uk/update.htm, has therefore been set up to notify readers of important amendments. All constructive criticisms and suggestions are particularly welcome and will be posted to the web-site, if relevant. Please send your ideas and corrections to me by e-mail to john@mccullagh.demon.co.uk Your contributions will be acknowledged on the web site and in future editions of this book. The more people who make suggestions, the better this book will become in future.

In a few places I have said "he" when it was difficult to construct a non-gender-specific sentence. Some of my examples are centred on Lasham, but they should be understandable elsewhere. I hope that I have been unbiased otherwise.

As ever in British gliding there is the usual mixture of units: knots, kilometres, feet and metres to help us to practise our mental arithmetic. A conversion table is at the end.

PREFACE TO TWELFTH EDITION

The syllabus for the theoretical knowledge for the licensing of glider pilots throughout Europe has been agreed. The full transition to EASA licenses will take several years but the Bronze Paper is being updated during this year to reflect the additional requirements and so the book has been expanded to take this into account. I have put in a brief explanation of skew-T diagrams as a result of popular demand, but a full explanation would need a book in itself.

Please contact me (john@mccullagh.biz) if you would like to make any constructive input for the thirteenth edition. Any amendments to be included in the thirteenth edition will be published on the update page of the web-site http://www.mccullagh.demon.co.uk/update.htm

I am especially grateful to the following people for reading the various editions and for making suggestions:

- Ken Stewart
- Gareth Bird
- John Carpenter
- Edward Coles-Gale
- Dave Eade
- Chris Gibson
- Jack Harrison
- Roger Hurley
- Frank Jeynes

- Chris Melsom
- Tim Moran
- Dennis Pasco
- Peter Reading
- Dr Tony Segal
- Bill Thorp
- John Travell
- David Williams
- Peter Wyld

I made many subsequent changes to the drafts that these people read, and then made many changes in the later editions, so any remaining errors are entirely mine.

John McCullagh
January 2012

John McCullagh has been a member of Lasham Gliding Society in Hampshire since 1982 and has been instructing since 1992. He has all three Diamonds. When not in the back seat of a K13, he can often be found flying his ASW27 around the UK and in the French Alps.

AIR LAW - INTRODUCTION

Introduction

As the title of the first chapter of a book, Air Law probably is one of the most off-putting. Fortunately it is not too difficult to understand the regulations that allow us to fly. Furthermore the subject has been broken up into more digestible chunks by creating several smaller chapters.

Where the law comes from

In 1944, 52 countries signed a document called the *Chicago Convention*, but there have been many new joiners and modifications since. The Convention established an organisation called The International Civil Aviation Organization (ICAO). ICAO is now an agency of the United Nations. Do not confuse it with IATA which is just for airlines.

The Convention defines international standards for aviation in matters such as airspace, aircraft registration and safety. Since aviation often involves crossing frontiers, all aircraft should follow the minimum standards of this convention. This will give some comfort should you ever encounter a French glider coming at you head-on. Both of you will (or at least should) give way by turning right.

Although the *Chicago Convention* only makes recommendations, the UK uses these as the basis of its statutes. The statutes include the *Air Navigation Order* (ANO) and several other statutory instruments.

To UK law must be added the requirements of the European Aviation Security Agency (EASA) for airworthiness and eventually on licensing. EASA is a body of the European Union which defines even more detailed common standards for European countries. Previously the civil aviation authorities of European countries co-operated though Joint Aviation Authorities (JAA) though a series of requirements, the *Joint Aviation Requirements* (JAR). JAA is gradually being absorbed in EASA. EASA's regulations and UK law are enforced in the UK by the Civil Aviation Authority, a government agency.

EASA's regulations can be found at:
http://easa.europa.eu/level1/enlangverstempl.html

Key ICAO standards

You need not know much about each article of the *Chicago Convention* except a few important provisions:

- Each state has sovereignty over its airspace
- Every aircraft shall comply with the rules of the air
- Radios may only be used by flight crew issued with a licence (UK law differs here - see later)
- Every aircraft must have a certificate of airworthiness
- The crew must have certificates of competency issued or validated by the state.

The Convention has eighteen 'annexes' with titles like "Personnel Licensing" and "Rules of the Air". These contain the detailed recommendations.

Publications

To comply with the Chicago Convention, each country's aviation authority issues publications describing its detailed operational arrangements. For all countries the key publications are:

- The *Aeronautical Information Publication* (AIP)
- *Notices to Airmen* (NOTAMs)
- *Aeronautical Information Circulars* (AIC)

In the UK these publications are produced by the Aeronautical Information Service (AIS), which is part of National Air Traffic Services (NATS).

Like all ICAO countries the UK publishes an AIP. It describes airspace; obstacles; wave windows for gliding; the facilities at each aerodrome; navigation aids; and services for weather, search and rescue and air traffic control. If you want to know the exact co-ordinates of some controlled British airspace, or the directions of the runways at an airfield, the UK AIP is where you should look.

NOTAMs (see later) describe temporary or permanent changes to airspace and aerodromes. For example, if the Red Arrows wanted to put on a display in the UK or someone wanted to fly a kite to a great height, a notice for everyone else to stay clear would be published in a NOTAM.

The Air Information Circulars (AICs) are published monthly and contain permanent amendments to airspace and charts, advice on operational, safety and administrative matters.

All AIS's publications are available on website of the Aeronautical Information Service (registration is free). http://www.ais.org.uk

Summarised information about the current NOTAMs and other temporary changes can be obtained from AIS as a Pre-flight Information Bulletin (PIB).

Another piece of terminology is Aeronautical Information Regulation and Control (AIRAC). This is the procedure in the *Chicago Convention* that ensures all this information from AIS is published around the world for the benefit of anyone who may be flying into the country. The AIRAC procedure also ensures that enough notice is given before a change becomes effective.

In addition to meeting its international obligations, the CAA publishes a wide range of other documents on many aspects of aviation such as radio procedures, engineering issues, safety, human factors and accident reports. These are available from its web site.

The British Gliding Association
The British Gliding Association (BGA) has been responsible for gliding in the UK since the sport started here. Over the years the BGA has satisfied the authorities that it is able to control the clubs, the gliders and the pilots. The certification of pilots; airworthiness; the registration of gliders; the training of instructors and engineers; and the investigation of minor accidents had all been delegated to the BGA.

This position is changing. More functions will come under the direct control of the Civil Aviation Authority, though some delegation will continue. At the time of writing the BGA's own publication *Laws and Rules for Glider Pilots* still contains important operational regulations and recommended practices (see later chapter). A prudent pilot would do well to observe them. A court of law that was considering a case of negligence would not be impressed if you had disregarded them.

The next chapters on air law & op procedures
After this fairly academic beginning, the remaining chapters on air law are more practically based. These chapters are:
- Airmanship and rules of the air
- Altitude
- Airspace
- Visibility
- Key operational procedures

It is planned that the topics covered in this first chapter and the five listed above will cover the Air Law and Operational Procedures paper that all pilots will eventually have to take before going solo.

Summary
This chapter can be summarised as saying that throughout the world all pilots follow a broadly similar set of rules. In the UK these rules have been codified by The *Air Navigation Order 2010*. Detailed operation matters are defined by AIP and any changes appear on AICs and NOTAMs. The regulations on airworthiness and soon on licensing are defined by EASA.

Questions
1. What international organisation defines minimum standards for air navigation?
2. Where would you look for a list of temporary hazards that you could encounter today?
3. What publication gives the recommended procedures for aerotowing gliders?
4. What document contains information about specific aerodromes, dimensions of airspace and other aeronautical services?
5. What does 'ANO' stand for?

AIRMANSHIP AND RULES OF THE AIR

Introduction

Airmanship can be defined as good decision-making, good manners, defensive flying and applying common sense. This chapter describes some of the related rules and procedures.

Risk of collision

The greatest risk that glider pilots face is collision, so a good look-out is essential at all times. It is the responsibility of "the commander of an aircraft to take all possible measures to ensure that his aircraft does not collide with any other aircraft."

The most likely places that you will encounter another aircraft at the same height are when you are on the circuit into an airfield and when you are in a local thermal, so vigilance should be greatest here.

However, you should also appreciate that the risks of collision continue when flying cross-country. This is because gliders do not spread out evenly, but will congregate in good lift, under cloud streets, near turning points, at other airfields and where the airspace channels them. Elsewhere the random chance of an encounter with another aircraft, though less, is still significant.

The risk of collision not only arises from other gliders, but from other users of airspace. These are usually light aircraft, but you can expect to encounter small passenger aircraft, military aircraft (from small jets to large transports), paragliders, hang-gliders, micro-lights and balloons. They will also congregate near their own sites, in airspace channels and near radio beacons.

Many power-pilots incorrectly assume that they will be warned by radio of conflicting traffic. Their aircraft will also maintain the desired height and course with very little intervention. Consequently some power-pilots may spend less time looking out than glider pilots. In addition, gliders have small cross-sections and are easy to miss. Glider pilots have to compensate for this by even greater vigilance.

Fortunately the sky has a large volume and random separation <u>usually</u> works, but this is not a guarantee. The greatest protection is provided by keeping a good look-out, not flying in another glider's blind-spot, fitting a FLARM anti-collision device and by staying well clear of cloud.

Closing speeds

Distant aircraft with a small cross-section can appear very quickly. Spotting these needs great vigilance and better eye-sight than is specified by the number-plate test for driving.

A glider approaching your thermal may appear as a small object when you first see it, but after you make one more thermalling turn, it will be a kilometre closer. Furthermore, the other pilot may still not have seen you.

The head-on image of an aircraft is initially small, and will grow in size only slightly, until close to impact, where it suddenly appears to 'explode' into the field of view.

30 sec from collision
2.4 km away. Closing speed 150 knots

10 sec from collision
800 metres away

3 sec from collision
240 metres away

If you hold this page one metre away, the images above are about the same apparent size as in reality.

Although the closing speed of two gliders might be 150 knots, a light aircraft and a glider may have a closing speed of over 200 knots. The time available to react is reduced proportionately. Moreover, a military jet may have a closing speed of over 600 knots, reducing the reaction time in the diagram above by a factor of four, but fortunately military jets, when operating at this speed, tend to be either lower or higher than gliders, except in mountainous areas where gliders and military jets can be at similar heights.

If you spot a potential collision hazard, just turning the glider will increase its visibility and will increase the chance of the other pilot also taking avoiding action.

Vision and look-out

The detail that we see across our field of view varies because of the structure of the retina at the back of the eye. This can be divided into three areas:

- A small oval shape (the fovea) that subtends only about 3° comprised of receptors called cones, where we see detail in colour
- A secondary area comprising a mix of cones and other receptors called rods with worse resolution
- A third area of peripheral vision comprising only of rods, which are mainly sensitive to sudden movement.

Rods are not as sensitive to colour. Consequently vision is increasingly monochromatic as images move away from the central fovea. We can only resolve any detail in a very small arc of vision. (Try fixating a word in the middle of the page and then recognizing adjacent words.)

Each eye also has a blind spot where the optic nerve connects to the retina. An object that is focused just on a blind spot will not be seen by that eye. Normally you use two eyes, but if anything obstructs one eye, such as the canopy frame, the other eye can miss things.

Be aware that when a pilot is operating with an empty field of view such as blue sky, the eyes will tend to focus at a point 1 to 2 metres away. You must actively look for objects on which to focus, such as the horizon, or even just the wingtips.

How to look out

An effective technique for looking-out is a habit that must be learned. Even if you are looking out most of the time, it is still easy to miss other traffic, unless you look systematically. In mountains the irregular background can reduce the contrast of another aircraft's image even more.

It is easy to become fixated on just one thing instead of looking out all around regularly. This object could be the next cloud, just one of the gliders in your thermal, the instruments, the map, your lunch or something on the ground. By concentrating on just one object, you can easily miss another aircraft nearby.

As mentioned already, our field of view can be divided into three areas: a small oval shape where we see detail, a second area with worse resolution and a third area of peripheral vision, which is mainly sensitive to sudden movement. (The 3° of primary vision is not much larger than the area of a full-sized altimeter on the instrument panel as seen from the pilot's seat.)

The secondary area is inadequate to notice a small but rapidly closing object. You must, therefore, methodically fix your gaze in each direction to use your primary vision. Do not just swivel your head about without pausing.

Try to maintain a steady rate of scanning throughout the flight rather than ten minutes of extreme scanning followed by very little.

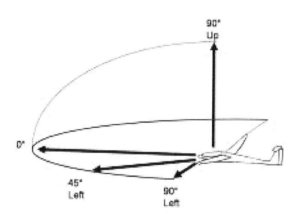

Half the scan cycle. At each point in the horizontal cycle, look above and below the horizon.

Look ahead, then horizontally to the side at 45° and then at 90°, or more if possible. At each of the horizontal points, also look above and below the horizon. Look overhead, and then check the attitude and perhaps the instruments, before checking the other side of the glider. This cycle should be repeated as often as possible.

Note that the greatest risk comes from other aircraft that are at the same height. They will therefore be on or near the horizon, and may be difficult to spot against this background. Consequently looking up at clouds or down at the ground does not count as a major part of your look-out. A threat can easily appear within 30 seconds, so if you have not looked all round for this long, you are trusting in another pilot's look-out.

If an object does not seem to move across your field of view, it is on a collision course. There is a saying "Constant bearing = constant danger". Furthermore, if the threat is not moving across your field of view, it will not be picked up by your peripheral vision, because this part of your vision is not sensitive to stationary objects. Read that sentence again. It means that if you do not look directly at the threat, you will not see it.

<u>Displaying a poor look-out is a certain way to fail a check-flight. You will not be allowed to fly solo again until a good look-out habit has been learned.</u>

Looking before turning
In your early flying lessons you were probably taught to look where you will be turning before you started to turn. However, looking in just one direction is insufficient.

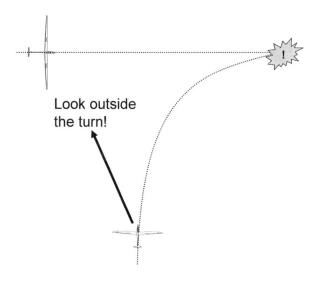

However a rapid 180 degree scan just as you turn is not practical. You should therefore have done your clearing-lookout well beforehand by scanning from the outer wingtip.

Just before the turn, look beyond the wingtip in the direction of the turn and then back over the nose before turning. Once turning you will need to check the horizon for speed control, but you also need to keep checking inside the turn and elsewhere.

Although the other aircraft should see you, do not rely on this; the pilot may be distracted and could be looking elsewhere.

In the diagram below, the right-hand glider might be even further behind and so would be invisible from the left hand glider, until the pilot started the turn. A continuous look-out during the turn is therefore essential.

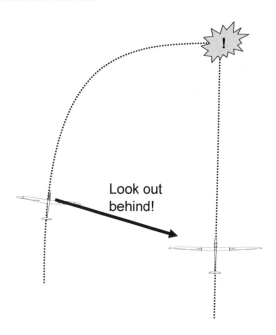

Looking out in thermals
Special considerations apply when thermalling with other gliders. Not only should you monitor all the gliders in the thermal, you must also continuously check that no-one else is about to join or fly through the thermal.

Gliders should circle in the same direction in a thermal, and gliders already established in the thermal have the right of way. If someone joins your thermal at a similar height and circles in the opposite direction, they probably have not seen you. Even if you found the thermal first, change direction to prevent a conflict or, if necessary, leave the thermal.

Join thermals at a tangent to the circles of the existing gliders, ensuring that the gliders already turning are not forced to make a manoeuvre to avoid you.

Pilots should keep to the principle of 'see and be seen'. Wherever the lift may be, your first responsibility is to keep the other gliders where you can see them AND where they can see you. You must be able to keep track of all gliders in your vicinity.

Waving at the other pilot in a shared thermal is not only friendly, but confirms to the other pilots that you have seen them.

If you lose sight of another glider in a thermal, leave the thermal. Look around especially outside the turn before straightening up. You must get clear of other gliders, however low you are, or however good the thermal is. It is just not worth risking a collision.

If you are thermalling at the same height, stay on opposite side of the circle, even if the other pilot has not, in your opinion, fully appreciated where to find the best lift. If you start chasing another glider's tail, the other pilot has lost sight of you, and is probably cursing you. This may mean that you have to adjust your speed, or to adjust your rate of turn to match that of the other glider. These rules still apply in gliding competitions.

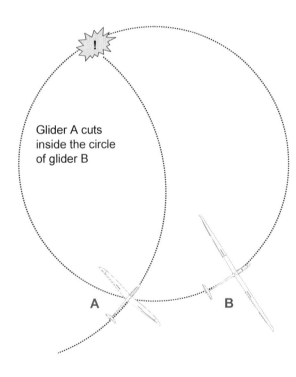

Glider A cuts inside the circle of glider B

A   B

Other points to bear in mind in a thermal are:
- Never turn inside the circle of another glider
- Never fly towards or ahead of another glider
- Never fly directly below another glider. They could dive to pick up speed or even spin. You should not fly under another

thermalling glider unless there is at least 200 feet of clearance
- Never fly in a blind-spot. For example, a position that is almost alongside would give you little chance, were the other glider to turn suddenly.

Some thermals have two cores so that you might find that the circles of two gliders intersect. This is highly dangerous. It would be much safer if you matched your circles in the same core.

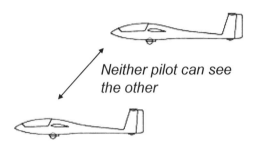

Neither pilot can see the other

A big risk occurs when one glider is flying slightly above and behind another. Neither can see each other. The upper glider cannot see through the floor and the lower glider cannot see behind. Be aware when 'dolphining' that another glider can be in this position.

Right of way when converging

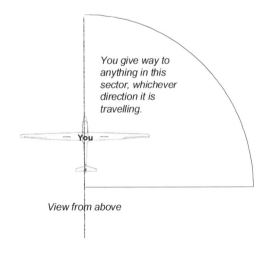

You give way to anything in this sector, whichever direction it is travelling.

— You —

View from above

The rule on converging aircraft is simply expressed as: if you see an aircraft on your right-hand side, give way to it. Alternatively you can say 'If it's on your right, it is in the right.'

Head-on

The rule for head-on aircraft is that both should turn to the right (in plenty of time, unlike the diagram below).

The fastest way to get a safe distance between you and the other aircraft is to move vertically, ie dive or climb, but this assumes that the other aircraft does not do the same, so a turn away is also needed

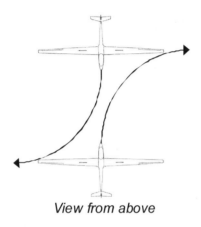

View from above

Hill soaring

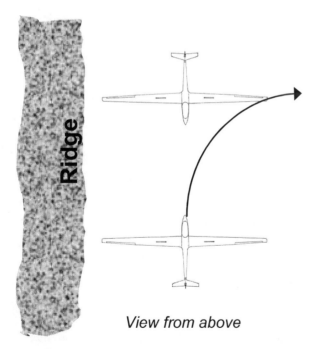

View from above

When flying near hills and mountains, all turns must be made away from the hill. On a ridge the same rule about head-on aircraft also applies, except that one aircraft may be unable to comply without

colliding with the terrain. Any glider on a beat with the hill on its left has a particular responsibility to keep a good look out, and to give way in plenty of time. Since a glider may suddenly turn away from the hill, you should only overtake another glider on a hill by flying between the glider and the hill.

Because they may have to give way, gliders flying with the ridge on their left should fly further out from the ridge than those with the ridge on their right.

Overtaking

Away from the hills, an overtaking aircraft should keep out of the way of the slower aircraft. In the UK gliders can pass either side of each other, whereas powered aircraft only overtake on the right.

Landing

If two gliders are landing together, the lower aircraft has precedence, but may not cut in front of another which is on final approach, nor overtake it. If you are aware that the other aircraft is making an emergency landing, you must give way to it.

"Steam gives way to sail"

Gliders shall give way to balloons, though you have the right of way with airships. Powered aircraft should give way to gliders, but do not rely on it.

Following landmarks

If you are following a road, railway, the coast or another linear landmark, you should keep right, so that the landmark is on your left. (British roads and railways tend not to be straight for very long and so compliance by gliders is uncommon.)

On the ground

After landing you can turn to clear the runway, if it is clear. If you are unsure where someone is landing alongside you, it is safer to land long and to taxi straight. The convention is that if you are overtaking another aircraft on the ground, you should land to the right of it, but most gliding sites have local procedures.

As you might expect, flying machines and vehicles shall give way to aircraft which are taking off or landing. Vehicles, and flying machines which are not taking off or landing, shall give way to vehicles towing aircraft. Vehicles which are not towing aircraft shall give way to aircraft.

Even if you have right of way

There is little satisfaction to be had after a collision even if you point out that you had the right of way. You can never assume that you have been seen, and you should always be prepared to take avoiding action.

Take the safe option

There are a myriad of situations where you can choose between a risky and a safe option, and it is not proposed to list them all here. The choice that you make may not be the direct cause of an accident, but may be part of the chain of events.

For example, you are flying downwind in a circuit with a much higher performance glider in front which is at about the same height. This glider will probably fly downwind further than you would want. You could wait until you get too low, or you could take the safe option of turning in early, well before the other glider, and landing further up the field to avoid a potential conflict.

During a flight the controls seemed stiffer than usual. There is a temptation to believe it was your imagination. After landing, it is essential to get it checked out, after ensuring that no-one else will fly the glider in the meantime. Bear in mind that the next pilot may encounter severe difficulties if the problem got worse. If you did nothing and a serious accident occurred, you would have to live with your conscience.

While doing a DI, you see a small fault but you are uncertain whether it makes the glider serviceable. The thermals are already booming and you think that the fault will probably not be a problem, especially since the previous day was normal. However, you have a small doubt. You should already know the answer to this dilemma. If in doubt, take the safe option. Remember that taking-off is optional but landing is compulsory.

Aerobatics

The CFI of your club is responsible for authorising aerobatic flights and has defined an area and minimum heights at which aerobatics may be performed.

Do not attempt aerobatics unless:
- You have received training
- Your glider is cleared for that type of manoeuvre and you have read its flight manual
- The weather is suitable
- You are current in that type of glider and for that manoeuvre
- Your glider is fitted with a serviceable g meter.
- You are clear of a congested area (ie a town, industrial or recreational area)
- You are wearing a parachute

Always keep your hand on the air-brake lever when performing aerobatics, or you might accidentally lower the wheel or the flaps in an attempt to control your speed.

If more than the maximum load is registered, usually 3.5g, the glider should be grounded until it has been inspected. You should also consider further training before flying aerobatics again.

Before any aerobatic manoeuvre and before practicing stalls and spins, you should perform the HASSLL checks:
- Height (sufficient?)
- Airframe (cleared for this manoeuvre, within placard limits and configured eg flaps, g-meter reset)
- Straps (tight?)
- Security (no loose objects?)
- Location (not over a built-up area or another airfield, and not in controlled airspace)
- Look-out (no aircraft nearby or below?)

Low flying

Gliders must not fly within 500 feet of any person, vessel, vehicle or structure without written permission from the CAA.

Specific exemptions to the 500 feet rule exist for hill soaring, for normal take-off and landing and for life saving. Exemption also exists for competition flying, but only when within a horizontal distance of one kilometre of the persons gathered to witness the event. Detailed procedures have been defined for competition finishes.

Except with the permission in writing of the CAA, an aircraft flying over a congested area of a city town or settlement shall not fly below a height of 1,000 feet above the highest fixed obstacle within a horizontal radius of 600 metres of the aircraft. The definition of a congested area is thought to include any urban area that is marked in yellow on the half million scale map. An aircraft flying over a congested area of a city town or settlement shall fly at least at a height that will allow the aircraft to land clear of the congested area.

Except with the permission in writing of the CAA, an aircraft shall not fly over an organised open-air assembly of more than 1,000 persons below a height of 1,000 feet, or below a height at which the aircraft could not land clear of the assembly, whichever is the higher. This part of the rule does not give an exemption for landing and taking off. A normal circuit over the Glastonbury Festival for a field landing would therefore be illegal.

Dropping objects

You must not drop anything from a glider, except for: persons by parachute in an emergency; articles for the purpose of saving life; ballast in the form of fine sand or water; or tow ropes at an aerodrome; and/or water that has been used as ballast.

Flying at another site

Flying from another airfield is useful experience, and should be tried, even if you can only fly dual. You may be on vacation or your visit may be an unplanned stop on a cross-country flight and you merely want another launch to be on your way. However you should always be aware of the additional stress of an unfamiliar airfield.

Whatever the reason for your visit, you must always spend time understanding the local practices and rules, such as:
- Do they require a check-flight before you fly solo?
- In which direction do you tow to the launch point?
- How do you queue to launch?
- What is the system for log-keeping including logging of your return?
- Do I need temporary membership?
- How do you pay for the flight?
- What signals are used for launching?
- Do they use high-tow or low-tow on the aero-tow?
- How does the winch behave?
- What are the options after a launch failure?

- Are there special considerations in certain wind directions?
- To where should I ask the aero-tow to take me?
- Are there known areas of lift, sink, turbulence or curl over?
- Are there airspace restrictions?
- Are there any other local hazards?
- Are you happy about flying near a hill?
- Is there other traffic such as powered aircraft or parachuting?
- Are there minimum heights to return to the airfield?
- Are there places to lose height if you are coming down from a great height?
- What are the circuit patterns?
- Are radio calls needed to launch or to land? In what language? What frequency?
- Where do you land, and to where do you taxi?
- How do you comply with local laws about pilot licensing, glider licensing and insurance?

All this additional information and the unfamiliar surroundings will increase your stress, so you may be a less able pilot than normal. Think through each stage of the flight carefully before you take off.

Summary

Ensure that you understand the following points:
- Where the risk of collision is greatest
- How to look out systematically and effectively
- Avoiding collisions and looking out in thermals
- Rights of way
- Rules for hill soaring
- Rules for aerobatics
- Low flying limits
- Stress levels when first flying at another site

Questions

1. You have dropped a bolt and it has disappeared under the seat-pan of your glider. You have declared 300km and cumulus has started to appear. What do you do?
2. You are flying with a ridge to your left. Another glider is coming the other way. What should you do?

3. What mnemonic should be used before aerobatic manoeuvres and for what do the letters stand?

4. What angle does your field of primary vision subtend?

5. How should you look out systematically?

6. You are approaching a large town into a headwind at 1000 feet AGL, but you hope to pick up some lift over the town, so that you can get to your home airfield, which is beyond. What should you be thinking about?

7. What is the minimum height needed to perform aerobatics over a town?

8. You see a powered aircraft coming from your left, what should you do?

9. Can a glider fly at less than 500 feet above the ground when it is not taking off or landing?

ALTITUDE

Introduction
It is essential to know how high you are and how high you should be, but your altimeter does not give you a simple answer. This chapter describes how to use your altimeter in different circumstances. Even if you are just local soaring, you will need to know the height in relation to any nearby airspace.

Pressure and altitude
We live at the bottom of an ocean of air. At the bottom of this ocean the pressure is greatest, and it is constantly changing because of the weather.

The pressure is commonly reported in units called millibars, which are abbreviated to mb. However the 'hectopascal' is now the standard unit, but fortunately this is identical to the millibar. It is abbreviated to hPa. (If you fly in other countries, you might also encounter pressure readings in inches of mercury or even millimetres of mercury.)

At sea-level the standard pressure has been defined as 1013.2hPa, usually rounded to 1013hPa. If you climb 27 feet above sea-level, the pressure falls by about one hectopascal. However this reduction in pressure with height does not continue at a constant rate as you climb higher. For most gliding purposes up to about 8,000feet, 30 feet per hPa is a good average. Note that by 20,000 feet the average rate is 1hPa per 50 feet.

Altimeter errors
Altimeters in gliders work by sensing the air pressure as the glider climbs and descends. Altimeters are therefore just well calibrated barometers, and so they are subject to several errors.

Firstly, some altimeters stick when you are climbing or descending. As a result you cannot expect them to be accurate, even on a short, local flight. Below 500 feet you often can judge height by eye more accurately than by using the altimeter.

In addition to sticking, there are other reasons why you cannot completely trust your altimeter, however much you tap it. (Incidentally, altimeters are delicate instruments and should not be tapped directly. Tap the panel beside the altimeter instead.) The altimeter will also fail to give an accurate height because the atmospheric pressure changes throughout the country and throughout the day. Power pilots often reset their altimeters as they move about the country, but glider pilots usually avoid this chore by allowing a large enough margin for error.

There are also much smaller errors because altimeters are calibrated by assuming an International Standard Atmosphere. The conditions where you are may be different.

Because of the errors of any altimeter, do not assume that it will accurately show your height to the nearest foot. Also bear in mind that the thermal may continue to take you higher after you straighten up, or the sink will continue to take you lower, long before you have cleared the airspace boundary. A good margin of error should therefore be allowed near airspace (about 200 feet).

The wake vortex from a heavy airliner, perhaps at low speed and high angle of attack, descends behind it and may give problems to gliders a considerable distance below its flight path. The CAA warns that the wake of a very large aircraft such as the Airbus A380 may cause difficulties as much as 1,000 feet below it.

Altitude

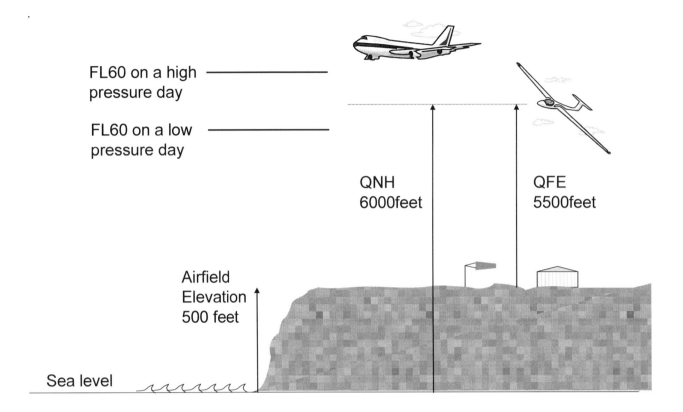

FL60 on a high pressure day

FL60 on a low pressure day

QNH 6000feet

QFE 5500feet

Airfield Elevation 500 feet

Sea level

Altimeter settings

An altimeter does not necessarily show the height above the ground. It merely indicates a distance from a selected datum. By adjusting the sub-scale knob, you can choose one of three datums: QFE, QNH and International Standard Setting. When set to QFE the vertical distance is known as height; when set to QNH the vertical distance is known as altitude and when set to the standard setting the altimeter shows flight level.

QFE

Zeroing the altimeter before take-off is known as setting it to QFE. You might remember the abbreviation as 'field elevation'. (The 'Q' comes from the days of Morse code.) This is convenient for local soaring, because the altimeter will show the absolute height above your home airfield with reasonable accuracy, though it will be affected by the errors described earlier. The QFE setting need not be for your home airfield; you can also call up another airfield to get the setting for its QFE.

QNH

The air pressure at mean sea level is known as the QNH. With the local QNH set on the subscale the altimeter reads altitude.

If your airfield is at an elevation of 500 feet above sea-level, turn the knob to add another 500 feet to the altimeter reading. Remember the abbreviation by thinking of it as nautical height.

With the altimeter set to QNH it allows us to readily monitor our clearance from obstacles shown on a map and also to check on our clearance from controlled airspace. Although QFE is the appropriate setting for local flying, it is not relevant when you are out of gliding range of your home airfield.

In the UK you should launch on QFE and should stay on QFE until you depart from the locality of your home airfield. When you set off to fly cross-country, is it recommended that you set the altimeter to show your altitude above sea-level. However, with the altimeter set to QNH, you have to become even more aware of the height of the terrain below. In countries with higher airfields than the UK, you may have to set the altimeter to QNH before launch.

Note again that the term 'altitude' in aviation means very specifically the vertical distance from sea-level. If you fly using QNH, your altimeter shows your <u>altitude</u>.

Standard Setting

Your third choice of altimeter datum is Standard Setting. This setting is important because some airspace is defined with reference to it.

Standard Setting is obtained by turning the sub-scale of the altimeter so that it reads 1013hPa. The altimeter set in this way will only show a correct altitude when the sea-level pressure just happens to be 1013hPa. At all other times, the altimeter is just measuring a pressure on a common basis. When the Standard Setting is used, the altimeter reading is known as the 'pressure altitude'.

The advantage of the Standard Setting is that all aircraft are using the same datum, even if they fly though places with different QNH pressures.

Flight levels

The Standard Setting is used to define flight levels. Flight levels are named by removing the last two zeros from the pressure altitude, so FL55 is at 5500 feet pressure altitude. The flights levels only ever step up in units of 500 feet, eg FL55, FL60, FL65 etc.

Flight levels are used to define the upper and lower limits of airspace such as airways and parts of some control areas and control zones. For example, the base of an airway may be defined at FL55. On a day when the sea-level pressure is 1013hPa, this boundary will be at 5500 feet above mean sea-level (AMSL). However, on other days FL55 will be found at other altitudes depending on the atmospheric pressure at that place. On a high pressure day you have to go higher before the air pressure falls to the pressure that defines each flight level.

This provides a slight, but fortuitous, safety margin for thermalling glider pilots. We tend to fly higher in thermals on days with higher pressure. On the days when sea-level pressure is over 1013hPa, the flight levels at the base of an airway will be at higher altitudes. For example if the actual sea level pressure is 1023hPa (10hPa above the standard), the bases of all the flight levels will be about 10x30= 300 feet higher.

Altitude and other airspace

Note that airspace restrictions can be defined using either altitude or flight levels. For example, where the London TMA is shown on the chart, this is always as feet AMSL whatever the flight levels are doing. If you see 5000´ on the chart, it means 5000 feet altitude. However many airways and some danger areas are shown as flight levels, not as heights above the ground.

The exceptions are busy airfields which are surrounded by an air traffic zone (ATZ). These zones are always defined in relation to ground level, and extend to 2000 feet above the airfield, not relative to sea level.

If you are asked at what level you are, you should say whatever you can see on your altimeter, followed by 'QFE', 'QNH' or 'flight level'.

Transition altitude

Separation of powered aircraft when under Instrument Flying Rules (IFR) (see later) is achieved by the aircraft using different flight levels depending on their direction of travel. This procedure starts above an altitude, known as the 'transition altitude'. Above this altitude under IFR, power-pilots change from using QNH and switch to flight levels.

The transition altitude is now at 6000ft throughout the southeast of England and will probably be at 5,000 or 6,000 ft for the whole country soon. This means that the bases of some low controlled airspace that had previously been expressed as a flight level are now expressed as an altitude. For example FL45 would no longer be relevant. Any airspace that was defined by FL45 would be defined by 4500 feet altitude. Other countries have different transition altitudes.

In the UK on days when the sea-level pressure is less than 1013hPa, FL60 would be below 6000 feet, and so it would not be used on these days in areas where the transition altitude was 6000 feet. The first available flight level would therefore be FL65. On high pressure days, FL60 will be above 6000 feet. It will then be the first available flight level. On the high pressure days there is also a gap between 6000 feet and the first available flight level, which is known as the 'transition layer'.

The altimeter puzzle and flight levels

You are flying at an indicated 5500 feet after taking off from an airfield that is at 500 feet. You had set your altimeter to QFE and the sub-scale reads 998hPa. You are now approaching an area marked as having controlled airspace at FL60. Do you have a problem?

Altitude

The answer is yes, because you are now forced to do some mental arithmetic that would be taxing in a Bronze Badge exam, and which is going to be even more difficult while flying.

Step 1   Find your true altitude
In our problem, you know that the airfield is 500 feet above sea-level and yet you treated that elevation as zero when you set QFE. Step one is therefore to add the airfield elevation to the altimeter reading to get your true altitude. Your altitude is therefore nearer to 5500+500 = 6000 feet.

However FL60 will only be at 6000 feet altitude on a day when the sea-level pressure is 1013hPa. A further correction is needed.

Step 2   Find the pressure difference for today
The second step is therefore to work out the difference between today's sea-level pressure and 1013hPa. You can work this out, because you know the pressure at your airfield from the sub-scale on the altimeter. Knowing this pressure and the elevation of the airfield, you can calculate today's pressure at sea-level.

Divide the 500 feet for the airfield's elevation by 30 feet per hPa. This gives you roughly 17hPa of additional pressure at sea-level. (This part of the calculation is always the same, whenever you fly from this airfield.)

Today, therefore, the subscale on your altimeter, as it is currently set, would read 998+17 =1015hPa if you descended to sea-level. This is 2hPa more than the standard 1013hPa, which translates back into 60feet (2 x 30feet per hPa).

When there is high pressure, the flight levels go higher. In our problem, FL60 is therefore only 60 feet above you. This is much too close for comfort because of the errors of your altimeter. The problem also would have distracted you for too long. It would have been less stressful to have tackled this problem before you took off by using the procedure in the next paragraph.

Before you take off
You may plan to fly near airspace defined by flight levels. If so, as part of your pre-take off checks, note on a piece of paper, the subscale reading when the altimeter is set for QNH. Also note the subscale reading for QFE. You will now be able to adjust the altimeter at will throughout the flight to:

- QNH as you set off cross-country,
- QFE when landing at the same airfield,
- Standard Setting of 1013 when near airspace that is defined using flight levels.

This is less likely to cause an error because it requires no mental arithmetic.

Altimeter setting regions
On the half-million-scale chart you will see boundaries labelled with the names of altimeter setting regions eg Chatham ASR & Barnsley ASR. These are where power pilots reset the altimeters to regional QNH after a radio call. This has only been mentioned here in case an ASR boundary (a line of double-crosses) is mistaken for the boundary of some airspace.

The boundary between two ASRs runs from top right. The diamonds from top left show the boundary of an Area of Intense Aerial Activity.

Summary
Ensure that you now understand:
- The fall in pressure with altitude
- The errors in altimeters
- The three altimeter settings
- The setting to be normally used when setting off to fly cross-country
- Flight levels and how they change with pressure
- Why you should note the sub-scale readings on your altimeter before take-off

Questions
1. You are flying with your altimeter set to QFE above your home airfield which has an elevation of 618 feet AMSL. Above you is Class A airspace that is marked on the chart as 5500´. The sub-scale on your altimeter reads 1002hPa. How high can you fly above the airfield before you infringe the controlled airspace?
2. You are climbing towards the lower limit of Class A airspace. What factors might affect

your decision about the level at which you will leave the thermal?

3. You are flying cross-country with your altimeter set to QNH. You are near Compton Abbas airfield which has an ATZ. The airfield is marked on the chart with an elevation of 811 feet. How high AMSL must you be when you fly over the airfield to be clear of its ATZ?

4. What settings from your altimeter should you note before you fly cross-country?

5. You have decided to fly cross-country using QFE. The airfield is at 618 feet and the sub-scale reads 995hPa. What would your altimeter read at the base of FL60?

AIRSPACE

Introduction

Glider pilots must ensure that they are familiar with the regulations about airspace wherever they fly. Clearly a collision with another aircraft would endanger many lives, but even just a close encounter could bring draconian restrictions on gliding. Any pilot found deliberately or negligently penetrating controlled airspace without clearance is liable to prosecution. Even if the perpetrator has not been identified by the authorities, if you see an incident, the incident should be reported to your Chief Flying Instructor. The risk of not reporting breaches is that the offender may make worse infringements and may even risk lives in future.

Source of airspace information

The standard reference that defines all UK airspace is the *UK Aeronautical Information Publication* (UK AIP) which is published by National Air Traffic Services (NATS). This is available either as hard copy, though there is always a risk that a binder has not been updated, on CD-ROM and on-line via the Internet. Registration on the Internet site is free. http://www.ais.org.uk/aes/login.jsp

Supplements are published monthly as Aeronautical Information Circulars to give notice of permanent changes to airspace as well as revisions to airfield data.

Organisation of UK airspace

UK airspace up to FL245 is divided into two Flight Information Regions (FIR) for administrative purposes, London FIR which is south of latitude 55°N, and the Scottish FIR, which is north of 55°N. Above the FIRs are Upper FIRs (UIRs).

In the FIRs and UIRs, the airspace can be classified as: A, C, D, E, F and G, largely complying with the International Civil Aviation Authority (ICAO) standards. There is currently no Class B airspace in the UK. Class A has the most stringent rules about its use and Class G is the least stringent. Classes F and G are both 'uncontrolled' airspace.

Class A airspace

Gliders must not penetrate Class A airspace, unless there is a specific agreement. You must be

specifically briefed on these agreements and comply with their conditions before you enter this airspace.

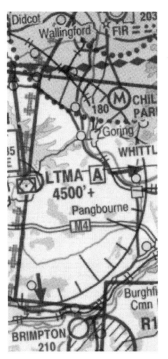

Here the London Terminal Manoeuvring Area (LTMA) extends upwards from 4500 feet above mean sea level from southeast of Didcot and almost to the air-strip at Brimpton. (The LTMA is at different heights elsewhere.) The A in the oblong shows that it is Class A airspace.

Terminal Manoeuvring Area (TMA) is a volume of controlled airspace set up at the confluence of airways in the vicinity of one or more major airports.

Class C airspace

The whole of the airspace above FL195 in the UK is classified as Class C airspace. Gliders without transponders are allowed to fly in designated gliding areas in some of this Class C airspace but with restrictions. These areas must be activated by gliding clubs using agreed procedures. With the exception of Aboyne, the Temporary Reserved Areas for gliding, TRA (G), will normally be activated only at weekends or public holidays. Aboyne will be able to request daily for the activation of their TRA (G) with two hours notice.

If you are in Class C airspace, you must listen on the correct radio frequency and you must remain in Visual Meteorological Conditions (VMC): 1500 metres horizontally from cloud, 1000 feet vertically from cloud and in 8km flight visibility. There are additional procedures for flying above FL240, but these are beyond the scope of this book.

Pilots flying in Class C must carry "a means of navigation" to give their position; GPS is sufficient.

Your altimeter should be set to the standard setting of 1013.2hPa. Clubs in wave-flying regions will provide a comprehensive briefing on the local agreements, radio frequencies and procedures.

Transponders

After 6 April 2012 gliders must use a Mode S transponder

- when flying at or above Flight Level 100 (unless it is in an active Temporary Reserved Area for gliding),
- when flying under Instrument Flight Rules in controlled airspace (unlikely except by accident), or
- when flying in controlled airspace of Class A, B or C or any other airspace (called transponder mandatory zones (TMZ) notified as requiring a transponder.

Class D airspace

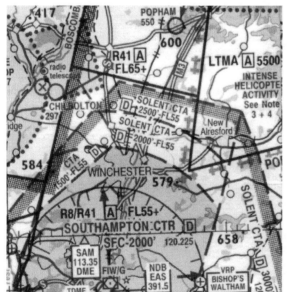

The portion of the chart above shows the Class D airspace in the Solent CTA and CTR in 2004. Note the dashed and shaded northern boundary of the CTA. It crosses the M3 at 2500 feet AMSL and changes direction southeast of the service area marked with an S on the road running north/south.

If there are clear advantages of flying through Class D airspace, glider pilots can fly through it, if given

clearance. However, you should spend the minimum amount of time there. You should particularly avoid flying near the runway centre lines. Tasks involving several gliders should not be set through Class D airspace.

Glider pilots must obtain clearance to enter any Class D airspace. However if you have accidentally strayed into Class D airspace, it is better to call up the Air Traffic Control (ATC) for that area, than to remain silent. Gliders show up on radar and it is probable that the controllers are already aware of the problem. Explaining your intentions to ATC should reduce this problem.

Note that during your transit of Class D airspace, the VMC minima for aircraft flying at less than 140 knots are:

- at 3000 feet altitude or below: clear of cloud and in sight of the ground and 5km of flight visibility
- above 3000 feet: 1000 feet vertically from cloud or 1.5km horizontally away from cloud in 5km flight visibility

Remembering these clearances and judging distances from cloud is difficult, so these rules may be simply remembered as staying well clear of clouds while in controlled airspace.

Class E, F and G airspace

Where Class E airspace exists, any glider can penetrate this without clearance, provided that they can comply with VFR, which are the same as for Class D airspace. No radio is required.

There are advisory routes (ADRs) for airliners that are classified as Class F airspace. They are 10 nautical miles wide. These may be crossed by gliders but caution should be exercised. Again, no clearance is required.

Class G airspace is all other airspace not covered by the other classes. Class G airspace is known as 'open FIR airspace'.

Airways, control zones and control areas

Airways are corridors, usually 10 nautical miles wide. They are almost always Class A. Gliders must not enter Class A airways unless there is a specific exemption. Note that temporary Class A airways may also be established by NOTAM to protect flights by royalty and other dignitaries (see *NOTAM* chapter). These must also not be entered.

Airspace

Control zones (CTRs) extend from the ground to a specified altitude or flight level around some airfields. Some are Class A such as Heathrow, and must not be entered by gliders. Others such as Lyneham CTR are Class D, and may be entered with a specific clearance from a controller. Some in Scotland and Northern Ireland are Class E.

Control areas (CTAs) and Terminal Manoeuvring Areas (TMAs) start at a specified altitude and have an upper limit. Some of these are Class A, eg around Heathrow, and so gliders must not enter, unless special arrangements have been made. However it is possible to enter the CTAs that are Class D eg Lyneham and Solent, after receiving clearance. Those that are Class E require no clearance at all.

Calling up a controller

Because you would be talking on a non-gliding frequency, you should have an R/T licence. The following sample conversation is therefore only given for background. It is not part of Bronze Badge and is not a substitute for attending a course and getting an R/T licence. You can therefore skip this section.

To enter Class D airspace, follow this procedure:
- Listen before you speak. There may be a conversation in progress already
- You must call up the ATC <u>well before entering the zone.</u>
- Call the ATC unit and give your full call-sign, eg "Brize Norton Glider Golf Charlie Alpha Bravo Charlie"
- They may abbreviate your call-sign and say "Bravo Charlie, pass your message".
- You should then give your
  Type
  Position
  Altitude
  Proposed track
- For example "Bravo Charlie is a standard/open class glider. Five miles east of Northleach at 3500 feet QNH. Heading one three five towards Wantage."
- They may say "Bravo Charlie cleared to enter Brize Zone not below altitude 2000 feet on QNH 1021. Maintain VMC. Report when entering zone".
- You reply "Bravo Charlie is cleared to enter Brize zone. Not below 2000 feet on a QNH of 1021. Will report entering"
- They will then acknowledge

- Stay on the frequency so that you can comply with their instructions.
- Fly straight on the proposed track. If you want to stop and thermal, call the ATC again and ask permission to thermal. For example, "Bravo Charlie. Request permission to thermal". Again repeat any clearance and report when back on track.
- If you want to change course, say to avoid cloud or to avoid sink, ask the controller for permission to change course.
- On leaving the airspace call the ATC again to notify them and change frequency.

Controllers only recognise two types of glider, Standard Class or Open Class, when judging how fast you will lose height. You should decide whether your glider is nearer in performance to a Standard Cirrus or a Nimbus before you call.

Scattered around the zones on the half-million maps are visual reporting points (VRP), which should be used when giving your position.

Brize Norton may give instructions based on its own QFE rather than sea-level. Its QFEs is 288 feet above sea level.

If you use Class D airspace, the BGA would like you to send a form to the CAA, with a copy to the BGA, which describes the service received. One form can cover several separate events. It can be downloaded from:
http://www.gliding.co.uk/forms/classdcrossing.pdf

Aerodrome Traffic Zones (ATZ)

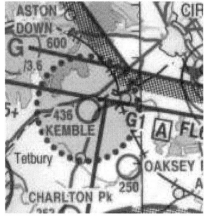

The ATZ around Kemble airfield is shown as a dotted circle. The height of the airfield is 436 feet, so this ATZ extends to 2436 feet AMSL.

Many airfields have an Aerodrome Traffic Zone (ATZ) around them during published times. Some of these are busy and so you must call on the published frequency before you infringe the zone (Air Navigation Order). While you are in the zone, you must stay on the frequency. If there is an air traffic controller, you must ask permission. Without radio contact you may cause a nuisance and possibly a serious danger. Even if there is only an information service or even no ground radio at all, other traffic at other zones will be grateful to know of your presence and will give information for you to judge your safety.

The airfields that have ATZs are marked on the half million scale chart by a circle of maroon dots and the whole zone is shaded in the same colour.

The length of the main runway determines the size of the ATZ. However the length of the runway is not marked on the half-million-scale charts. You should therefore assume that every ATZ is the maximum size. The maximum size of an ATZ is 2000ft above airfield level, and 2.5 nautical miles RADIUS from the mid-point of the longest runway.

Note that the ATZ is defined by the height above the ground as measured at the airfield. To calculate the altitude of the top of the ATZ, you must find the elevation of the airfield on the chart and add 2000 feet. You should compare the result with your own altitude above sea level (QNH), NOT your height above your home airfield.

If you are at 2000 feet above the ground and at least 2.5 nautical miles away from an airfield, the angle that you look down to the airfield will be less than 8 degrees. If you are looking down by more than 8 degrees and are at less than 2000 feet above the ground, you are in the zone. (8 degrees are not easy to judge but twenty degrees should be obvious and should alert you to call the airfield.)

Even if you are outside an ATZ, you should avoid staying any longer than necessary in line with the active runway. Powered aircraft may fly straight for a considerable distance after taking off and before landing.

Military Air Traffic Zones (MATZ)

In addition to an ATZ, many military airfields are surrounded by even larger zones, known as military air traffic zones (MATZ). These zones usually consist of a 5NM radius circle and a 4NM wide stub protruding 10NM away from the main runway. In the circle the MATZ extends from the surface up to

3000 feet above airfield level. In the stub it goes from 1000 feet to 3000 feet above airfield level.

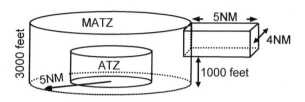

Gliders can penetrate MATZ provided the ATZ is not penetrated. Radio contact is therefore not mandatory in the MATZ. However the CAA it is strongly recommends that you call on the published frequency at least 5 minutes' flying time before you expect to enter the MATZ, and comply with requests from ATC. As ever, care should be taken, particularly when crossing the centre line of the runway.

The Benson MATZ is shown by the larger dotted circle and shading and the shaded stub extending north northeast. The smaller dotted circle is the ATZ

Prohibited, restricted and danger areas

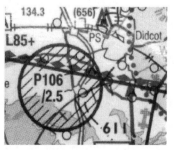

The prohibited area P106 at the nuclear research establishment at Harwell (SW of Didcot) up to 2500 feet AMSL

Airspace

In addition to controlled airspace, there are other areas that have restrictions for various reasons. Full details can be found in the UK Aeronautical Information Publication, but they are also marked on the half-million-scale chart.

The areas are shown on the chart with a code number and a designated altitude in thousands of feet below which the limitation applies. The first digit of code number gives an approximate latitude, eg D216 is north of 52 ° N.

In prohibited areas all flight is prohibited. They are shown on the chart as an area that is marked with a solid maroon circle and diagonal hatching. For example, P106/2.5 is at Harwell southwest of Didcot and it extends to 2500 feet altitude. If you think you are in a zone, then leave immediately by the shortest route.

Restricted areas

Restricted areas are shown on charts in the same way as prohibited areas, but flight may be allowed subject to certain conditions. Some of these conditions are printed on the half-million-scale chart, eg the prohibition of helicopters and microlights below 2,400 feet altitude near a prison in R214/2.4 near Milton Keynes. Gliders can therefore penetrate some restricted areas, but not all.

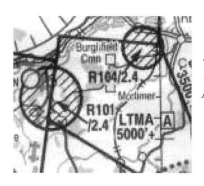

The restricted areas at Aldermaston and Burghfield are both prohibited to gliders.

Danger areas

The third of this group is the danger area. These have a prefix of 'D'. Sometimes the altitude is very high or even unlimited. For example, D128/1.4 OCNL 50.0 means that occasionally this danger area extends to 50,000 feet but sometimes is only to 1,400 feet. Some danger areas are marked as 'UNL' ie unlimited height.

The dangers include weapons firing ranges, unmanned drones, tethered balloons, target-towing

and parachute drop zones. These areas are often subject to military by-laws, and trespass would be an offence as well as being dangerous.

Some danger areas are only active during published hours. These are shown as solid maroon lines with diagonal hatching. Some danger areas are only activated through a NOTAM. These are shown with a dashed boundary.

The Sennybridge Danger Area in South Wales is an Army range. The asterisk means that the airspace is subject to bye-laws. It applies to 23,000 feet but occasionally to 50,000 feet.

Unlike prohibited and restricted areas, most danger areas have a Danger Area Crossing Service (DACS) or Danger Area Information Service (DAIS), which you should contact if you wish to fly through. The Information Service will just tell you if the zone is active or not, whereas the DACS must give a clearance (or not). Frequencies are shown in the notes on the half-million-scale chart. As ever, if you do not get positive clearance, assume that the area is closed.

The dialogue for an unsuccessful request to a DACS might go as follows:
Pilot: Westbury Approach, G-ABCD request Crossing Service for Danger Area 113
Westbury Approach: G-ABCD, Westbury Approach, Danger Area 113 active, remain outside.

Where possible, the pilot should provide the DACS unit with an estimated crossing time, eg
Westbury Approach: G-ABCD request Crossing Service for Danger Area 701A between 1430 and 1445
Westbury Approach: G-ABCD, Westbury Approach, Danger Area 701A crossing approved between 1430 and 1445, report vacating
Pilot: Danger Area 701A crossing approved between 1430 and 1445. Wilco G-ABCD

Bear in mind that landing in an area with craters and unexploded munitions would be hazardous, so you should avoid getting low in these areas, even if you get clearance.

Some danger areas such as rifle ranges have upper limits below 500 feet AGL, and are not shown on the half-million-scale chart. (They are listed in UK AIP.) If you are flying below this height, you are probably going to land and so you should specifically look for such hazards when choosing your field.

Parachute drop zones

Abingdon parachute zone and the extra circle with a G to show that it is occasionally used for gliding.

On the half-million-scale charts, you will see parachute symbols at many airfields throughout the country. In these zones, parachutists could be free-falling from Flight Level 150 (ie about 15,000 feet). They are impossible to spot until their parachutes open, and so in these areas there is a major risk of a fatal collision.

The zone is usually a circle of 1.5 nautical miles radius but there can be exceptions (currently Keevil zone has a 2 nautical miles radius). However, in a strong wind they may start their descent from a position well outside the drop zone, so you must keep well away from the upwind side of the zones.

Do not assume that there will always be a NOTAM to tell you when parachute zones are active. The operators of these airfields only have to notify the authorities on the day.

The frequencies of the drop zones are listed in the table of information on the half-million-scale chart. If you wish to pass near to a drop zone, you should call up the frequency. An R/T licence is not required to make this call. Simply say for example:

- Glider: "Brize Norton, Glider Golf Charlie Alpha Bravo Charlie"
- ATC: "Bravo Charlie, pass your message"
- Glider: "Is the South Cerney parachute drop zone active?"

- ATC: They will then give the status. (If negative, they will probably say that they have not been notified of any activity.)
- Glider: "Roger"

If there is no answer, assume that the zone is active. The drop zones at Hinton-in-the-Hedges, Langar, Peterborough/Sibson and Weston-on-the-Green are particularly busy. Weston-on-the-Green is even marked as a danger area.

In addition to the permanent parachute drop zones, there are military exercises and air-shows throughout the year at other places. These will be notified through a NOTAM. Look in particular for any navigation warning with the abbreviation PJE (parachute jump exercise).

Obstacles

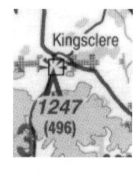

The Kingsclere mast northwest of Basingstoke is 1247 feet above sea level and 496 feet above ground level.

Obstacles over 300 feet high, such as radio masts, are shown with two heights. The large number is the height above sea level, but in brackets in smaller numbers is the height above the ground. Note also that there are flare stacks over oil refineries can send flares up to 600 feet high which are invisible in bright sunlight.

The chimneys (as opposed to cooling towers) from power stations emit hot gases at high velocity. Do not fly low over these. Even higher up, the air can be very rough and could cause a spin.

Gas venting sites

In 41 places in the UK a circle marked on the chart with the letters 'GVS' warns of possibility of extreme turbulence caused by the emergency venting upwards of very large quantities (the pipes are up to 90cm in diameter) of natural gas at supersonic speed. Do not fly over these places.

Airspace

High Intensity Radio Transmission Areas

Most High Intensity Radio Transmission Areas such as Croughton (north of Bicester) and Oakhanger (south east of Alton, Hants) should not affect the pilot but they may affect radios and other electronic instruments. Note that emissions from Fylingdales in Yorkshire are dangerous to human health, if you get too close and/or stay too long.

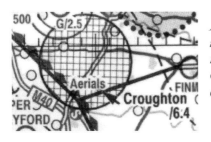

Area of high intensity radio transmission at Croughton up to 6400 feet AMSL

Areas of Intense Aerial Activity

Areas of Intense Aerial Activity are marked where traffic is likely to be intense. In this example, Oxford AIAA is around Brize Norton's CTR. You can enter these areas but a good look-out, as ever, must be maintained.

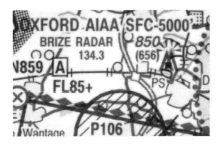

The Oxford Area of Intense Aerial Activity from the surface to 5000ft AMSL. A line of blue diamonds shows the boundary on the chart.

Other airfields

Keevil airfield is 200 feet above sea level. /3.2 means that the cables could extend to almost 3200 feet AMSL (3000 feet above the surface) when the 2 nm radius parachute zone to FL150 is not active.

At other gliding, hang-gliding and paragliding sites, winch-launching may be in progress up to 3,000 feet above ground level. There is a separate chapter on the hazards of landing at other airfields.

Even if an aerodrome has no Aerodrome Traffic Zone, the pilot of any aircraft flying in its vicinity must comply with the Rules of the Air Regulations and stay clear of it.

Other hazards

In addition to parachute zones, danger areas, prohibited areas and restricted areas, other hazards include:

- Air to Air refuelling, Military Training Areas, Aerial Tactics Areas and Military Reserved Airspace – some of these are in upper airspace and many are also over the sea.
- Military Low Flying – this can occur anywhere in the UK, but generally takes place at heights of 250 feet to 600 feet AGL.

Planning your flight

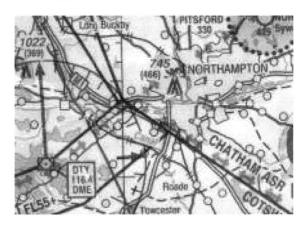

Northampton West is a popular turning point and is near the edges of several areas of airspace. The boundaries are the straight lines. If you fly in this area, look at your map to see which area has a lowest limit.

It is important to plan any cross-country flight before you take-off. You should draw your planned course as a line on the half-million-scale chart. You can then review the airspace at each point on the route to decide how close you are to the boundaries. (See *Navigation* chapter)

Be particularly aware of any airfields and parachute zones that you may fly near.

Airprox reporting

If you consider that you have been endangered by the proximity of another aircraft, you should make an Airprox report. Ideally you should report an Airprox immediately by radio, though this may be impractical for a busy glider-pilot. (London Information is on 124.6MHz, 124.755MHz or 125.475MHz and can supply information on a wide range of subjects in flight.) Otherwise note the exact time, level, place and the other aircraft type and, if possible, its registration. Make the report using the official form not more than seven days later. It will be investigated confidentially to improve procedures in future.

If you are considering filing an Airprox, or think one might be filed against you, you should contact a BGA airspace representative. Currently it is:

Bruce Cooper – 01628 521360
Bruce.cooper68@virgin.net

If you are carrying a flight recorder, keep the data. This can provide evidence against possibly exaggerated claims against you. Some GPS units have a quick 'man-overboard' facility that allows you to mark a place of interest.

Infringing

The following is a direct quote from the CAA:
"If you know you are infringing airspace, call on 121.5Mhz. The quicker you admit the problem, the quicker it can be resolved. Once controllers know where you are going, they can plan other traffic around you. The majority of airspace infringers are not prosecuted. If you realise that you have infringed and then alert ATC, you are reducing the risk of prosecution. However if you hide your infringement and act irresponsibly you are increasing the chance that the CAA will take action."

Code of practice near airspace

On some days it is possible to fly above Class D zones such as Brize Norton. You should nevertheless call them out of courtesy. Although you will appear on their radar, it does not give them your height. If you do not call, they will assume that you are in their zone, and divert other traffic five miles away from you.

The BGA recommends that glider pilots intending to stay outside controlled airspace but operating within 1nm or 2km horizontally from controlled

airspace, or flying over controlled airspace should endeavour to contact the appropriate Air Traffic Control (ATC) unit to explain their intention.

After making contact, the following information should be passed to the controller: glider position, height, intention (eg 'staying clear of the zone') and any service request (or 'no service required')

Final thoughts

Controlled and NOTAMed airspace always looks empty, except perhaps the flight-path into Heathrow. Do not be fooled into thinking that no-one is watching or that no-one really cares. You are on radar and you are often clearly visible from the ground and from other aircraft. Even a slight infringement will invalidate a badge claim and in a competition will cause a substantial loss of points. When cases are brought to court, the fines are usually in the thousands of pounds.

It is worth investing in an in-flight computer to alert you to nearby restrictions to airspace but you must be sure that the computer has been accurately loaded with the latest data about airspace. Flight analysis software is also useful to review your cross-country flights using the data from your flight recorder. The software should have a complete and up-to-date database of UK airspace plus NOTAMs, so that you can confirm to your own satisfaction that you remained within the law.

Summary

The following points must have been understood:
- Types of airspace and restrictions on gliders
- How to recognise airspace on the chart
- Size and status of ATZs
- Status of MATZs
- How to identify danger, prohibited and restricted areas
- The size and importance of parachute drop zones
- The need to plan your flight in advance
- Airprox procedures

Questions

1. You can comfortably fly above some Class D airspace without infringing it. Is any action needed?
2. How is the class of airspace shown on a half-million-scale chart?
3. What is the maximum size of an ATZ?

Airspace

4. How big is a parachute drop zone?

5. What are the two numbers beside high obstacles on a half-million-scale chart?

6. A hatched zone is marked P106/2.5. It is a Sunday. Do you need to call to get permission to cross below 2500 feet altitude?

7. You will be flying near an MATZ. What action should you take?

8. You have a close encounter with a light aircraft. What do you do next?

9. What does TMA stand for?

Also try the airspace quiz on
http://www.mccullagh.demon.co.uk/airspace1.htm

VISIBILITY

Introduction

You may take for granted your ability to see where you are going. This chapter describes the situations when you may not be able to see as far as usual, or as far as you are required by law.

Flying in cloud – risks

It is legal for a glider to enter cloud in the UK in uncontrolled airspace, but before you try this out, there are some regulations and advice to know about.

When you are completely enveloped in cloud, the lack of visual reference points can quickly produce complete disorientation. You may experience the sensation that you are turning when you are not, and vice versa. The sensations may also be misleading when trying to maintain a steady speed.

These misleading sensations mean that you have to rely on instruments. If you follow your instincts instead of your instruments, it is easy to lose control, exceed V_{NE} and seriously damage the glider. Before trying cloud flying on your own, you should therefore have training to fly on instruments. As a minimum, the glider should have a functioning turn & slip indicator, but preferably it should have an artificial horizon. A radio enables you to warn other gliders.

The other major risks of cloud-flying are obvious. You can lose track of where you are, or you can collide with another aircraft or the terrain in mountainous regions.

Be especially careful about skimming just below the base of a cloud street. The lift that attracted you may also attract other pilots, perhaps from the opposite direction with a high closing speed.

Accidental cloud flying

In hilly country cloud may form well below the general cloud base and may be lower than the high ground. This is known as 'orographic cloud'. It can develop rapidly and extensively.

If you become enveloped in cloud while ridge flying, you must act quickly. Turn to fly away from the hill and get out of the cloud. A gentle turn will be easier to control. If the wind is not at right angles to the hill, the minimum flying distance to clear the ridge is obtained by flying slightly into wind rather than directly at right angles to the ridge. Because you are flying into wind, your best glide speed will be 5-10 knots higher than for still air (see polar curves in *Aerodynamics* chapter)

If you have to enter cloud (for example by descending through it from a wave flight), fly away from any mountains, switch on the artificial horizon/turn & slip indicator in good time for the gyros to speed up, and open the airbrakes. Opening the airbrakes will help to control your speed. Fly straight as you enter the cloud, and then monitor the speed and the artificial horizon/turn & slip.

Because of the possible compass swings when you change speed, it is difficult to use a compass even to fly on a constant heading. Using the compass to change to a new heading is even more difficult, so fly as straight as you can.

Most artificial horizons take a few minutes to speed up and then require you to fly straight and level for a short while to set them. It is also possible that your battery has insufficient charge to power the artificial horizon. Consequently, if the flag has not yet disappeared, the gyro is not spinning fast enough and the instrument should be ignored.

Flying into wind, provided that is away from the mountains, will reduce your chances of being lost when you emerge, because you will have not covered so much ground. The wind at height is usually much stronger, so flying downwind could rapidly take you away from your current location.

If you are having problems stabilising your speed, there is another useful hint for an unplanned cloud descent. The needle on the air-speed indicator on all aircraft changes direction at the precise moment that the nose is level with the horizon. You should centralise the stick at that point. If you wait until the air-speed reaches your desired speed before trying to level out, you will set up a pilot-induced oscillation and you will quickly lose control.

If you find that your air-speed gradually falls to zero and stays there, your Pitot-tube has iced up.

Visibility

However with the airbrakes open, you can safely keep the stick forward of centre.

If you are lost above cloud in the mountains, call 121.5MHz, the distress frequency (see procedure in *Navigation* chapter). They can guide you away from danger.

Flying in cloud - procedures
The BGA's *Laws and Rules* states that "no glider shall enter cloud within a radius of 5 nautical miles of any gliding site except from at least 200 feet from below the lowest part of the cloud". The proviso allows cloud flying near a gliding club, but by requiring 200 feet of climbing in clear air before the cloud is entered; it prevents a glider flying into the side of a cloud near a gliding site. Note this rule applies to you if you are 5 nautical miles from any gliding site, not just your own.

Laws and Rules states that when cloud-flying, the occupants must be wearing serviceable parachutes and have been instructed in their use. However, elsewhere in *Laws and Rules* a recommended practice is to wear parachutes at all times, if the glider is built to accommodate them.

You should use your radio to announce on 130.4MHz that you are entering cloud. You should give your call-sign, height and position and say that you are entering cloud. If there is another glider in the same cloud, it is essential that you both call your heights regularly. (Note that only glider pilots use 130.4MHz; other traffic will be unaware of you.)

When you leave the cloud, announce your call-sign and the fact that you are now clear of cloud. Because cloud flying may require heights to be called, unnecessary chatter by other non-cloud-flying pilots on 130.4MHz should be avoided.

Visual Meteorological Conditions (VMC)
Every flight must be flown under either Visual Flight Rules (VFR) or Instrument Flight Rules (IFR)). The definition of the in-flight conditions to enable flight under VFR is called Visual Meteorological Conditions (VMC).

When the visibility is worse, IFRs apply. Instrument Meteorological Conditions (IMC) are the weather conditions in which it is not possible to comply with VFR.

VMC requires two conditions to be met – clearance from cloud and in-flight visibility. If conditions do not satisfy the VMC then they are deemed to be Instrument Met Conditions (IMC) and the flight must be flown under Instrument Flight Rules (IFR).

However in Class F & G airspace, there is no requirement for gliders to fly in VMC. Gliders can therefore enter cloud, provided that they follow agreed procedures. The detailed regulations about VMC refer only to flight in Class C, D and E airspace.

VMC is defined using a term called 'flight visibility'. Flight visibility, as opposed to meteorological visibility, means the distance that you can see directly in front of you at your height. Even if you are looking at the only cloud in the sky, if it is 500 metres away and the same height, then the flight visibility is 500 metres, and you are therefore in IMC.

The parameters for VMC are a specified clearance from cloud and a specified minimum in-flight visibility as estimated by the pilot through the canopy. The parameters depend on the classification of the airspace, altitude or flight level, and – for some airspace at or below 3,000 feet altitude – airspeed also. See the extract from the CAA chart on the next page.

In particular, for aircraft flying at 140 knots or below, in Class D and E airspace, when at or below 3,000 feet altitude, VMC requires the pilot to remain clear of cloud, with in-flight visibility of at least 5km and to remain in sight of the surface. If flying above 3,000 feet altitude in the same airspace the visibility required increases so that you must remain clear of cloud by at least 1,000 feet vertically and 1500 metres horizontally, with a minimum in-flight visibility of 5km. Above FL 100 the required visibility increases to 8km.

In Classes F and G airspace, for VMC when at or below 140 kt, at or below 3,000 feet altitude, the pilot is required to remain clear of cloud, with in-flight visibility of at least 1500m and to remain in sight of the surface.

Judging these separations is difficult, so the best advice is to stay well away from cloud in controlled airspace. If you are unable to maintain VMC and you are in controlled airspace, inform the controller.

Instrument Meteorological Conditions (IMC)

Outside controlled airspace one of the primary rules under IFR is the need to remain at least 1,000 feet above the highest obstacle within 5 nautical miles of the aircraft – known as the 'safety height'.

Above the transition level in IMC, power pilots can be expected to be flying at flight levels that depend on their magnetic track. This is known as the quadrantal height rule. Since gliders are always climbing or descending, the quadrantal rule is irrelevant to them. There are therefore no rules that apply to IFR flight by gliders outside controlled airspace. Collision avoidance is solely by 'see and be seen' and by radio on 130.4 MHz.

Experienced pilots sometimes ask for a Radar Advisory Service from a controller, for example when flying near wave clouds in case IFR traffic emerges close by.

Glider flight in controlled airspace under IMC is forbidden without clearance from the appropriate ATC authority, unless specific exemptions are notified. However for less experienced pilots, you should simply remember to stay in uncontrolled airspace and away from cloud-base.

UK AIRSPACE CLASSIFICATIONS

	Class A	**Class C**	**Class D**	**Class E**	**Class F & G**
Radio and ATC clearance required for IFR flight?	Yes	Yes	Yes	Yes	No
Radio and ATC clearance needed for VFR flight?	VFR flight not allowed	Yes	Yes	No	No
VFR minima	VFR flight not allowed				

This table is an extract from the full CAA chart and only contains the restrictions for aircraft flying at less than 140 knots indicated airspeed. See http://www.caa.co.uk/docs/64/200890108ATSAirspaceClassificationV3.pdf

Visibility

Darkness

Gliders can fly at night, but only if they are fitted with lights and if they have specific insurance cover. Night lasts from 30 minutes after sunset until 30 minutes before sunrise, as determined on the ground. Cloud cover will make it much darker at times. You should not, therefore, assume that the clock is the only deciding factor in determining acceptable light levels.

Be aware that at altitude the sun may still be visible above the horizon, but it may already be getting dark on the ground. Also be aware of the time it takes to descend from great height, so start your descent in good time to land in daylight.

Clean canopies and misting

A clean canopy is essential at all times, but a misted and/or dirty canopy is particularly lethal when flying into a low sun. When misting is likely, it happens more quickly on a dirty canopy

Recognise that there will be times when the canopy will always mist up dangerously, however much you try to avoid it. At this point, do not launch. Do not rely on the draught from flying to clear the mist. This could take several minutes and meanwhile you are flying blind. Bear in mind that you may be required to land within seconds after a launch failure.

If the canopy mists up in flight, which can quickly happen, open the DV panel and the ventilator to try to dispel the mist, even if it is cold. You are effectively cloud flying at this point, so follow the instructions above to stay in control and away from the terrain.

Visibility in rain and snow

Slight drizzle does not reduce visibility greatly, but heavy rain should be actively avoided. Snow has an even more dramatic effect on visibility and sight of the ground can be quickly lost. Do not fly when snow is imminent.

Summary

Ensure that you understand the following points:
- Risks of cloud flying
- Requirement for flying in cloud
- What to do if you accidentally enter cloud
- VFR and when it must be maintained
- Relevance of IFR to gliders
- Onset of darkness, especially at altitude
- Misting and safety
- Visibility in rain and snow

Questions

1. You are flying at 4000 feet altitude in uncontrolled airspace. What is the minimum visibility for you to fly there?
2. What are the risks of flying in cloud?
3. You are about to take a wire launch for a brief local flight. The weather was sunny but the sun set about five minutes ago. The canopy is misting up but this will clear shortly after you take-off. What decision should you take about the duration of this flight?
4. You decide to call up an ATC to cross Class D airspace above 3000 feet AMSL. They ask you to maintain VMC. What visibility do they require you to maintain?

KEY OPERATIONAL PROCEDURES

Introduction
This chapter contains some of the regulations and recommended procedures for some aspects of gliding that have not been covered in the other chapters, but it does not contain all the remaining operational regulations. It only paraphrases those that will be regularly encountered. The full laws and operational regulations are contained in the BGA's *Laws and Rules* which provide the definitive statement for gliding. You must also read this publication in addition to reading this chapter. A few helpful other hints have also been included in this chapter.

Responsibility of the pilot in command
No matter who got the glider out, rigged it and inspected it, the responsibility for the safe conduct of any flight lies with the pilot in command. The pilot must be satisfied before take-off that the flight can be safely made, that the aircraft and its equipment are fit for use, that the aircraft has been maintained in accordance with its certification, that the aircraft is correctly loaded and carries sufficient fuel and oil.

Aero-towing
You should already be able to aero-tow competently and so there are no detailed instructions in this section. However the risks from aero-towing have been identified by the BGA as being highest when:
- Using the belly-hook
- Glider's centre of gravity is near its aft limit ie you are a light pilot
- Cross-winds
- Turbulent air in take-off area
- Short tow-rope (length must never be less than 150 feet, ie 47 metres)
- Inexperienced pilot
- Inexperienced tug-pilot

The greatest risks come from flying too high behind the tug. The factors listed above each can contribute to this situation. Do not accept a tow when more than one of the listed factors applies.

The BGA also state that the sum of the aerotow launches made by the tug-pilot and the glider pilot in their respective capacities must not be less than six.

If when aero-towing, the tug rocks its wings laterally, you must release immediately. If you are waved off by the tug, or if the aerotow-rope breaks, do not attempt to turn back below about 200 feet. Landing straight ahead is safer, even if it is in a field with crop.

If you are unable to release from the aero-tow, you should fly out to the left and rock the wings. (This manoeuvre is more difficult than it sounds. You can only bank away from the tug. Banking inwards immediately brings the glider behind the tug.)

If the tug-pilot waggles the rudder whilst on tow, you should check that your air brakes are not open, or you should assume that your drag-chute has deployed. Close or jettison as necessary.

The commander of a tug / glider combination is the tug-pilot. The maximum length of the tow rope is 150 metres.

Winch-launching
A glider must not be launched by winch or ground tow above 60 metres unless the CAA has given written permission and the launch is in accordance with the conditions in that permission.

A weak link must be fitted to a winch or auto-tow cable unless the cable strength is below the breaking load approved by the glider's manufacturer or by the BGA's Technical Committee.

Further operational regulations on winching are contained within the BGA's *Laws and Rules*. Each club will also have its own detailed operating procedures for winch-launching and auto-towing.

Cross-country
The pilot in charge of a glider must not deliberately undertake a cross-country flight unless he/she has been permitted to do this. At present this means a Bronze Badge with cross-country endorsement or higher qualification. However if you have drifted away from the airfield, it is better to do a well-

Key operational procedures

planned and well-executed field landing than a highly marginal attempt to land back at the airfield.

Definition of flight

A glider is defined as being in flight from when it first moves to take-off until it comes to rest after landing.

Insurance

European regulations require that glider pilots are covered by a minimum level of third party insurance. The mandatory third party insurance requirements are ultimately defined by the European Commission in Special Drawing Rights and so these are subject to fluctuating exchange rate against sterling. Single seat gliders with a maximum take-off weight between 500kg and 999kg need, at the time of writing, £1.75m of third party cover. For two seaters it is £2 million.

Note that the insurers may set conditions such as a valid ARC or flight in daylight. If the conditions are not met, you are not covered. For example a hull damage claim was refused on the grounds that the pilot medical had expired just before the accident, even though there were no medical implications in the accident.

Glider registration

ICAO has allocated a nationality mark to each state. The UK has the letter 'G'. This is followed by four more letters. All gliders will need to carry a full G-registration after 28 September 2008. A Certificate of Registration is issued by the CAA at the same time as assigning a glider's registration. In addition all BGA gliders must display additional identification markings (ie the trigraph or competition number) to be displayed as large as practicable on each side of the fin and/or rudder of the glider in a substantially vertical plane. There in no requirement for this mark to be on the underside of the starboard wing.

ICAO also stipulates that all registered aircraft must carry a fireproof identification plate showing the registration mark, even though the incidence of spontaneous combustion of gliders is low.

The CAA maintains a register of aircraft. This is a public document and allows anyone to identify the owner, either in person, by phone or on-line. Owners are also required by law to inform the UK

CAA of change of ownership. Please also inform the BGA of any change of ownership.

Pilot's log-books

The registration of gliders brings glider pilots into a further piece of UK law. The Air Navigation Order requires that "Every member of the flight crew of an aircraft registered in the UK….shall keep a personal flying log book." This should be used to record all flights in ink at the end of each flight or as soon thereafter, as is reasonably practicable, including:

(a) The date, the places at which the holder embarked on and disembarked from the aircraft, and the time spent in flight

(b) The type and registration marks of the aircraft.

(c) The capacity in which the holder acted in flight (ie P1 or P2)

(d) Particulars of any special conditions under which the flight was conducted, including night flying and instrument flying

(e) Particulars of any test or examination undertaken whilst in flight.

The log-book must record the name and address of the pilot and any licences held.

Log books should be retained for two years, though in practice you will probably want to keep each log book for life.

Although ink is specified, the CAA also accepts computer output on paper. 24 hours between the flight and its recording in a pilot's log book is also considered acceptable.

Licences

At the time of writing the formal licensing of British glider pilots is in transition. EASA will define a minimum syllabus for the practical and theoretical training of recreational glider pilots. Even though national authorities may add additional detail, each country's licence will be recognised throughout Europe. A further licence may be needed for recognition in all ICAO countries. The licensing rules will include common medical standards and currency requirements.

Endorsements will probably be added to licences to allow cross-country flight and aerobatics. Additional ratings will be awarded for instructors and examiners.

Self-sustaining (turbo) gliders cannot launch themselves and for pilot licensing are classed as gliders. Self-launching motor gliders and touring motor gliders are classed as powered aircraft and the pilot already needs a PPL to fly one.

Driving licences

Whilst not part of the aviation examinations it is worth mentioning the law when glider trailers are towed. If you obtained a full driving licence before 1 January 1997, you can tow any trailer behind your car.

However if you got a standard driving licence after 1 January 1997, it sets a limit on the combined weight of the towing vehicle and trailer. The limit is set at a Maximum Authorised Mass (MAM) of 3.5 tonnes. The MAM of the trailer can be more 750 kg only if it weighs less than the unladen weight of the towing vehicle. In practice you can probably tow most 15 metre gliders but you are likely to exceed the limits with most open class or two-seater gliders. The BGA Laws & Rules has a full explanation, but it is mentioned here to alert some pilots to a potential problem, which might invalidate their insurance if ignored.

Buying a glider

Before deciding on what type of aircraft to buy, you should first check with your CFI to ensure it is a suitable type for someone of your experience. If it is unusual, check whether the model is type-approved. Both the CAA and EASA have web-sites of approved types. The BGA will provide much useful information.

All EASA aircraft must be registered with the CAA and issued with an EASA non-expiring Certificate of Airworthiness (C of A) and Airworthiness Review Certificate (ARC). Only specified vintage gliders, known as Annex II sailplanes, are eligible for BGA registration and issue of a BGA C of A.

It is strongly recommended that a BGA inspector or licensed engineer surveys the aircraft and its records before you buy it.

If the glider is CAA-registered (has a G-registration), both parties are required by law to notify the CAA and change the registration details within 28 days. Details are on the back of the registration document. The CAA make a charge each time there is a change in ownership and so syndicates are advised to register in the name of a trustee to avoid regular fees when the syndicate changes.

If you are buying or selling either am EASA or an Annex II aircraft you should also advise the BGA about changes of ownership. This allows the BGA to send important such as airworthiness information and ARC reminders.

Bird-strikes

A pilot must report to the CAA any bird-strike which occurs whilst the aircraft is in flight in or over the United Kingdom.

Formation flying

Aircraft shall not fly in formation unless the commanders of the aircraft have agreed to do so.

Laws & Rules

The BGA's publication Laws & Rules for Glider Pilots is the definitive source for some of the preceding regulations. It is available free as a pdf file on the BGA web-site.

Questions

There are no questions for this section because they would merely repeat the information already given.

RADIO

Introduction

This chapter covers the basics of what you should know when using a radio in a glider, or calling up a glider from the ground. Other chapters provide examples of the sort of things you might want to say to cross airspace and to land elsewhere.

Wireless Telegraphy (WT) Act 2006

It is an offence to install or operate aeronautical radio transmitting equipment in a glider or on the ground without a licence, whatever frequency you use in the air-band.

Application forms for aircraft and aeronautical (ground) station WT Act Licences can be found on the CAA website, together with additional information on aeronautical radio licensing, at http://www.caa.co.uk/radiolicensing. Contacts are:

Radio Licensing Section
Directorate of Airspace Policy
CAA House K6G6
45 – 59 Kingsway
London WC2B 6TE
Tel: 020 7453 6555
Email: radio.licensing@caa.co.uk

The same licence also permits the use of a hand-held radio in the specified aircraft as a back-up. Further information for recreational aviation can be found on the CAA website at http://www.caa.co.uk/default.aspx?catid=2004&pagetype=90&pageid=12107

Aeronautical radio equipment

Aircraft radio equipment must be an approved type listed either on the CAA Airworthiness database for Aircraft Equipment Approvals or on the European Aviation Safety Agency (EASA) website.

Operators' licences

Many private pilots have a Flight Radiotelephony Operators Licence (FRTOL). You have to pass an exam to get this licence. However Article 51 of the Air Navigation Order provides an exception for pilots from holding a licence on the condition that it is a private flight and the pilot does not communicate by radiotelephony with any air traffic service unit, flight information unit or air/ground communications service unit, ie communications are only permitted with recreational aviation aeronautical (ground) radio stations. This includes parachute drop zones.

In an emergency, a glider pilot may use the VHF Emergency Service frequency of 121.500 MHz without having a FRTOL.

The operator of an aeronautical (ground) radio station does not require a Radio Station Operator's Certificate of Competence, unless an Air Ground Communication Service or Air Traffic Service is being provided from that site.

Radiotelephony call-signs

Gliders should use in the order of preference: the registration letters or the competition number on the fin, all with the optional prefix 'glider'.

Vehicles should use the suffix 'mobile'. Other portables should use the suffix 'mobile', 'winch', 'launch' or 'launch-point'. Fixed locations should either use the suffix "base" or 'glider base'.

Note: The suffix "radio" is now reserved for Air Ground Communication Services only and should not be used elsewhere.

What to say on the gliding frequencies

The language used on air-band radio has very specific terminology that is designed to convey precise information in the shortest possible time when reception may be poor.

You can say a lot with very few words. This frees up time for other messages. Many people do not appreciate this and use the radio as a substitute for a mobile phone or as a CB radio.

Ideally, the radio should be used to transmit:

- Your position and intentions no more often than every 30min.
- Information about the weather, if you think conditions have changed
- Announcement of an imminent unscheduled landing
- Warnings of collision risks
- Training instructions

- Cloud flying warnings
- Changes to another frequency

Messages such as "I have found another good one here, Pete" at every thermal, clutter up the frequencies and prevent more important messages. Few messages are necessary when local soaring.

All messages must be as brief and as clear as possible. Remember, no-one else on the frequency can speak while you are holding forth, or when you are repeating an unclear message. Others' needs may be far greater than yours.

Calling someone else

When you first call someone, you give the call-sign of the station that you are calling, then your own call-sign. For example, to call glider 150 from glider 406, you say "150 406" and wait for a response.

Once you know they are on the frequency, for subsequent messages you can just say your message without calling them up first. This saves time.

When replying to the first call, you might guess that they just want to know your status without you being asked eg, "150 10 miles north west Swindon 3500". This will also save time. Alternatively, if you do not know what is being requested, 150 might say in reply "406 pass your message".

If using anything but a gliding frequency, use your registration in full. Only if a controller abbreviates it to the last two letters, can you also abbreviate it.

Like visible light, radio waves travel in straight lines. The horizon will therefore be the limit of VHF radio signals. Consequently, the range of your transmission increases with height. If you do not get a reply, wait until you have climbed higher and try again.

Terminology

There are precise words for common situations but, if you can't think of the correct official word, use plain English. The oddest terminology is the use of the word 'read' to mean receive. Most of the rest are fairly obvious, but here are some of the most common words and phrases:

Affirm	Yes (said as 'Ay-firm')
Acknowledge	Let me know that you have understood

Break	There will be a pause before the next part of my message
Cancel	Annul previous clearance
Changing to	My new frequency will be
Cleared	Authorised to proceed under the specified conditions
Confirm	I request verification of something
Contact	Call this station
Correction	I have made an error. The corrected version follows.
Disregard	Ignore what I just said
Expedite	Do this a fast as possible
Go around	Request for an aircraft to abandon its approach and to start again
How do you read?	How clearly are you receiving me? On a scale of one to five, five is excellent.
I say again	I will repeat what I just said
Monitor	Listen on this frequency
Negative	No, or permission not granted
Orbit	Circle at your present position or where instructed
Pass your message	Please tell me what you want. "Go ahead" is not approved in the UK
Radio check	Reply "Glider *your registration*. Reading you 5" if reception is good or else another number on a readability scale of 1 to 5
Read back	Repeat what I have just told you
Request	May I have the following service?
Roger	I have received your message (but it does not mean I will comply, see Wilco). 'Copy' is not approved.
Say again	Please repeat what you just said
Speak slower	Please speak more slowly
Standby	Wait for another message. I will call back shortly
Transmitting blind	I am not receiving from this station but in case anyone can hear me, here is my message
Tyro	Can be used as a prefix to your call-sign to signify that you are inexperienced
Unable comply	Cannot comply. Followed by a reason
Verify	Check and confirm
Wilco	Will comply. Your message has been received and will be complied with. Not to be used for ATC clearances.

Radio

You need not say 'Over' or 'Out' because the meaning is usually clear without these words. 'Over' means I am expecting a reply. 'Out' means the conversation is ended. The term 'over and out' is illogical, and only should occur in bad films. To acknowledge the receipt of a message you can also just repeat the sender's call sign.

Phonetic alphabet
The words in the tables below are used when individual letters and numbers are transmitted. The syllables to be emphasised are underlined.

Alpha
Bravo
Charlie
Delta
Echo
Foxtrot
Golf
Hotel
India
Juliett
Kilo
Lima
Mike
November
Oscar
Papa
Quebec (pronounced Keh-BECK)
Romeo
Sierra
Tango
Uniform
Victor
Whisky
X-ray
Yankee
Zulu

Emphasise each syllable equally eg ho-tell, dell-tah, no-vem-ber, yang-kee.

Saying numbers
Zeeroh (never as 'O')
Wun
Two
Tree (Not three)
FOW-er
Fife
Six
SEV-en
Ait
NINE-er (to distinguish it from fife)

Note that the only other numbers are 'HUNDRED' and 'TOUSAND' so that 11000 feet is said as "Wun Wun Tousand". 'Hundred' is used only when there are two zeros at the end eg an altitude of 5500 feet is said as "Fife tousand fife hundred". However, glider 150 is said as "Wun Fife Zeeroh", not "one fifty" nor is it "one hundred and fifty". The other numbers are just said in sequence. For example 130.4 would be said as "Wun Tree Zeeroh Dayseemal Fower".

Common faults
- Do not start talking until you have pressed the transmit button
- Do not talk until you are sure the current conversation on the frequency is over (You will hear a howl when someone talks over another message, and neither message will be heard)
- In your excitement check that you do not have your finger on the button. (If the radio goes quiet, it could be your fault.)
- Do not press transmit until you know what you are going to say
- If someone has not heard you, do not keep transmitting. There is no answer-phone. Wait a while before trying again. Say 'Nothing heard' so that someone who has replied knows that he was not heard.
- Do not engage in trivial chat or give a constant description of your progress.

If there is no answer, you should check that you are on the right frequency, that the set is switched on, and that the squelch control has not been turned too far.

Gliding frequencies
The following table outlines the primary and secondary uses of the gliding frequencies. The secondary use of the frequencies should only be made when the frequencies that are primarily used are very busy.

You may wish to write these frequencies on a label in the cockpit (plus those for any important airspace and any local airfields)

121.5	Emergency frequency
129.9	This is for ground to ground retrieval purposes only and is shared with other air sports such as parachuting

129.975	Common Glider Field Frequency (CGFF) - This is used by certain airfields within a range of 10NM of the site and up to 3000 feet.
130.1	Primary Use – Local flying and competition start and finishes. Local & other flying. Secondary Use - Lead and follow training.
130.125	Primary Use - Lead & follow training, and cross country location messages. Secondary Use - Local flying and competition start and finishes.
130.4	Cloud flying and cross-country messages.

Other key frequencies, such as parachute drop zones, are given on the half-million-scale map and on the card that accompanies it.

Mayday

If you have a life-threatening emergency, call 'Mayday' on whatever frequency you are on (or 121.5MHz if you think they could help more and you have time to change channels). No FRTOL is required. On 121.5MHz, call London Centre in south of 55°N, or call Scottish Centre north of 55°N, though they would reply whatever you called them.

There is an exact sequence of things to say, but you would be forgiven if you did not follow it. As you might expect, your message should consist of the following information:

- "Mayday, Mayday, Mayday"
- The station you are talking to
- Your registration
- The nature of the problem
- Your intentions
- Position
- Height
- Heading
- Any other useful information such as the number of people on board

If you call on 121.5MHz, do not leave that frequency without permission.

You can also use 121.5MHz on the ground (or any other frequency), if, for example, you were unfortunate enough to need medical assistance after a field-landing accident.

If anyone else calls "Mayday" on a frequency that you are using, keep quiet while the emergency is underway. There is probably not much you can do except record the information for the rescue services. If you are able to offer RELEVANT assistance, reply immediately. Otherwise keep quiet initially and write down what you heard. Then say that you have copied the Mayday and will relay it on the emergency frequency. If you then relay the message on 121.5MHz, use the words "Mayday Relay" to make it clear that you are not the subject of the emergency.

For non-life-threatening situations or emergencies that do not apply to you, you can also make a PAN call. (You can also downgrade your Mayday to a PAN.) For example you may be the first to spot a forest fire or you may see someone bale-out. Instead of saying Mayday three times, you say "Pan-Pan, Pan-Pan, Pan-Pan" on 121.5MHz. Then give details of the event. Stay on the frequency, until you are excused.

Training fix

You can practice making a call on 121.5MHz to get a position fix. Apparently the controllers welcome the practice as well. Tune to 121.5MHz and ensure that you have turned up the volume to hear what is being said. Listen for 2 minutes to ensure that a real emergency is not in progress. Transmit: "Practice PAN, practice PAN, practice PAN, *your registration* requires training fix".

Wait for a response. They should give you a position relative to a major landmark. Give them feedback on the accuracy. They will ask if you need another service. For example they can give you a magnetic bearing to any airfield in the UK. Before you leave their frequency tell them to what frequency you are changing back or they may assume that you really are lost with a radio failure.

Talking to controllers

You need FRTOL to talk to controllers. If a controller gives you instructions such as a clearance, you MUST repeat exactly what they tell you, especially a clearance and anything with numbers in it, such as an altitude, altimeter setting, frequency, runway and heading. 'Roger' or 'Wilco' is insufficient. At the end you should give your call-sign.

They may abbreviate your call-sign. Use your full call-sign until they shorten it. If you are Glider G-DABC, they may shorten it to Glider Bravo Charlie once they are happy that there is not another Bravo Charlie in the vicinity.

Occasionally you may hear an automatic recorded message. This is an ATIS, Automatic Terminal Information Service, and is continuously transmitted to provide pilots with weather and other information at specific airfields when there is no-one on duty.

Not everyone on a non-gliding frequency is a controller. Smaller airfields will not have a fully qualified air traffic controller at their radios. These airfields have the call-sign that includes 'Information' for a Flight Information Service (FIS) or 'Radio' for an Air Ground Communication Service (AGCS). Unlike controllers, they cannot give instructions such as clearances; they may only give information. You may still wish to repeat any information that they give you to check it.

The full procedures for radio telephony (CAP413) are given on the CAA web site.

Summary
The main points are:
- Get a FRTOL if you are likely to fly into or near airspace that may require you to contact an air traffic control unit
- Be brief
- Use the radio (whether or not you have a licence), if you are infringing airspace, near a parachute zone, landing at a strange airfield, in a danger area, if you are hopelessly lost near controlled airspace, or in any other emergency.

Questions
1. You have a 720 channel radio in your glider and a hand-held radio. You do not intend to talk to controllers. Do you need a licence?
2. Where do you find the frequency for the ATZ of a parachute drop zone?
3. What is the main purpose of 130.4MHz?
4. How would you spell 'chrysanthemum' in the phonetic alphabet?
5. You are asked to 'Read back'. What do you do?
6. How is an altitude of 1700 feet transmitted?
7. How is an altitude of 11,500 feet transmitted?
8. If you make a mistake when transmitting, what do you say?
9. What does 'Standby' mean?
10. What does a readability of '5' mean?
11. How would a ground station abbreviate the call-sign 'Glider G-CKDN'?
12. How is a frequency of 131.025 transmitted?
13. How do you say 'Yes'?
14. How do you say 'No'?
15. If you are told to do something but cannot eg 'maintain height', what do you say?

NOTAMS

Introduction

NOTAMs (Notices to Airmen) are published by each country's aviation authority to alert pilots to temporary hazards. These notices must be read before any pilot flies cross-country. The infringement of airspace in 2002 cost a private pilot £600 in fines and costs, because he had not read the NOTAMs. This chapter therefore provides a brief guide to getting the NOTAMs and to understanding them.

Sources of NOTAMs

All airfields should receive the NOTAMs and notices of permanent changes to airspace. They should display them for use by pilots. However you can also get them for yourself.

NOTAMs are published by National Air Traffic Services as part of its Aeronautical Information Services. They are available via the AIS web site:

http://www.nats-uk.ead-it.com/fwf-natsuk/public/user/account/login.faces

Access is free, if you just want the NOTAMs as plain text. If you do not have Internet access, you can also receive NOTAMs by fax.

Structure of NOTAMs

From the web site, first choose the NOTAM and VFR FIR Brief for either EGTT (London for southern Great Britain) or for EGPX (Scotland for the north). The London Flight Information Region (FIR) is south of latitude 55°N. The Scottish FIR is north of 55°N (roughly at Newcastle).

The NOTAMs are then grouped into two categories: aerodrome information and navigation warnings (aerial hazards).

Content of NOTAMs

NATS keep changing the format of NOTAMs, though the basics remain the same. If you view them on-line, there are two columns and some shading. For each Flight Information Region (FIR) the NOTAMs are grouped into the two main types.

For each individual aerodrome warning in the first column, the first item is the code for an airfield. For navigation warnings no airfield is involved and so the first item is a 'Q code'. This assists software in processing the NOTAMs. The NATS web site has a page that explains what this code means to a computer. The last few digits of this code give the coordinates.

After the Q-code, the start & finish dates and times are given. The start and end of the NOTAM is indicated by a ten digit year/month/day/time. For example 10/12/09 10:43 means that the hazard starts on 9th December 2010 at 10:43 UTC. UTC, Coordinated Universal Time, is virtually the same as Greenwich Mean Time, and it is used in NOTAMs even when British Summer Time applies.

Free format text describing the hazard is preceded by the letter E. An AUS reference number then appears - AUS refers to the Airspace Utilisation Section of the Civil Aviation Authority. The upper and lower altitudes are given where appropriate and then sometimes the start and finish times are given again preceded by the word 'schedule'.

Another reference number eg H2176/08 appears in the second column.

Sample NOTAM

In a typical NOTAM the first column will show something like:

Q)EGTT/QWPLW/IV/M/W/000/100/5038N00227W002
B) FROM: 11/04/30 09:00C) TO: 11/04/30 09:30
E) PJE WI 2NM RADIUS 5038N 00227W
(WEYMOUTH). CTC 01980 628211
11-04-0065/AS 3
LOWER: SFC
UPPER: 10000FT AMSL
H1121/11

The NOTAM above comes from a section called NAV warnings. The first line gives the Q code, in this case London (EGTT) for the south of Great Britain.

You can then learn that it applies on 30 April 2011 from 09:00 GMT until 09:30 on the same day. The free format description then begins with the letter E: parachute jumps were planned within a 2 nautical mile radius of Weymouth at N 50° 38′ W002° 27′

NOTAMs

from 10,000 ft QNH. (There is also contact number for the Red Devils Freefall team 01980 628211 and two reference number s 11-04-0402/AS 4 and H1121/11.)

Another example

Q) EGTT/QWALW/IV/M/W/000/025/5217N00040E002
B) FROM: 11/04/29 14:00C) TO: 11/04/29 17:00
E) AIR DISPLAY/AEROBATICS WI 2NM 5217N 00040E
(HENGRAVE HALL, BURY ST
EDMONDS, SUFFOLK) 11-04-0146/AS 2.
LOWER: SFC
UPPER: 2500FT AMSL
H1251/11

This NOTAM was also published in the nav warnings but could have been in the aerodrome section. It states that from 14:00 GMT on 29 April 2011 to 17:00 on the same day, there will several aerobatic displays near Bury St Edmunds up to 2,500 feet.

Look out particularly for NOTAMs involving about the RAF aerobatic display team, the Red Arrows. A formation of jets performing sudden manoeuvres is probably the largest, fastest and most dangerous aerial hazard that you could imagine, so stay well clear.

Restricted airspace may be created for various other reasons such as flights by royalty and other foreign dignitaries. Previously these were protected by what was known as purple airspace. Now temporary controlled airspace (CAS-T)), may be established in the RAC section f the NOTAMs. This section may also have temporary ATZs that are set up for events such as race meetings. For reasons of security the cause of this temporary airspace is often not published. Even though it is only Class D, glider pilots must not penetrate this airspace while this restriction is in force and will not receive clearance.

Abbreviations in NOTAMs

Some words have been abbreviated in NOTAMs in the past, though this is less common. This section provides some of the abbreviations that may occur in NOTAMs, though often these words are spelt in full. A full list of official abbreviations is in *UK Aeronautical Information Publication* in section GEN 2-2

A/A	air to air
A/AA	area of intense air activity
AAL	above aerodrome level
ABV	above

ACFT	aircraft
ACT	active
AD	aerodrome
AFT	after
A/G	air to ground
AGL	above ground level
AIP	Aeronautical Information Publication
AIP SUP	AIP Supplement
ALT	altitude (ie height above sea level)
AMSL	above mean sea-level
AVBL	available
AVG	average
AWY	airway
BFR	before
BLW	below
BRG	bearing
BTN	between
CONS	continuous
CTA	control area
CTC	contact number
CTR	control zone
D...	D followed by a number is a danger area
DEG	degrees
DEP	depart
DIST	distance
DNG	danger
DRG	during
DUR	duration
EG	code letters for the UK
EG..	often followed by codes for danger area, restricted area or prohibited area
EG..	if followed by two more letters, it is usually the ICAO code for a British airfield
EGPX	Scottish Flight Information Region (FIR)
EGTT	London Flight Information Region (FIR)
ELEV	elevation
ENR...	reference to the En-Route section of AIP Manual
EST	estimated
ETA	estimated time of arrival
ETD	estimated time of departure
EXER	exercises
FCST	forecast
FIR	Flight Information Region
FL...	flight level (when followed by numbers)
FLD	field
FLT	flight
FM	from

FREQ	frequency
FT	feet
GEN	general (reference to GEN section of AIP manual)
GLD	glider
GND	ground
H24	24 hours a day
HEL	helicopter
HGT	height
HR	hour
HZ	hertz
ICAO	International Civil Aviation Organisation
IFR	instrument flight rules
KM	kilometre
KT	knots
LAT	latitude
LEN	length
LGT	light/lighting
LONG	longitude
LVL	level
MAG	magnetic
MAP	aeronautical charts
MATZ	military air traffic zone
MAX	maximum
MDA	area designated for air combat training
MHZ	megahertz
MIL	military
MNM	minimum
MSL	mean sea level
NAV	navigation
NAVW	navigational warning
NBFR	not before
NM	nautical miles
NXT	next
OBST	obstacle
OHD	overhead
P….	prohibited area followed by a number
PERM	permanent
PJE	parachute jump exercise
POSS	possible
PSN	position
R….	restricted area followed by a number
RAD	radius
RA(T)	restricted area (temporary)
RDO	radio
REF	reference
RWY	runway
SFC	surface
SVFR	special visual flight rules
SUP	supplement (to AIP)
TEMPO	temporary
TFC	traffic

TIL	until
TWR	tower (aerodrome control frequency)
UKAIP	United Kingdom Aeronautical Information Publication
UNL	unlimited
U/S	unserviceable
UTC	Coordinated Universal Time
VER	vertical
VFR	visual flight rules
VRB	variable
WI	within
WID	width
WO	without
WRNG	warning

Reviewing the NOTAMs

It is often difficult to determine the areas that are covered by NOTAMs, because place names are not always used. Latitudes and longitudes, danger area codes and military exercise zones are often quoted instead, which take time to relate to a planned flight. However, if you routinely stay clear of danger areas, the activation of these will not be relevant to you. Places such as Flight Refuelling Areas are high up and usually way out to sea.

NATS provide software to review NOTAMs and instructions for its use are on the BGA web-site. However some think this software could be more helpful and so other free software exists for reviewing NOTAMs, notably Sky Demon. These other systems attempt to plot the positions of NOTAMs on a map, where there are sufficient data. Even the NOTAMs that cannot be plotted are nevertheless identified, so their relevance can be determined by reading them. There are differences in the approach in the various products, but each can help to find the important navigation warnings among the many that are hundreds of miles away or even offshore.

There is also a Freephone number (0500 354 802) that provides recorded information on temporary restricted airspace including the Red Arrows, but does not include all NOTAMs such as danger area activation.

Some latitudes and longitudes

The main lines of latitude and longitude are shown on the half-million-scale chart but the following summary may help you quickly dismiss the irrelevant NOTAMs:

57° N	South of Aberdeen, Braemar, Mallaig
56° N	Edinburgh, Dumbarton
55° N	Newcastle-upon-Tyne, Gretna
54° N	York, Morecambe Bay
53° N	Wash, Nottingham, Stoke, Snowdonia
52° N	Ipswich, Milton Keynes, Tewkesbury, south of Hereford, Fishguard
51° N	Romney, Petersfield, Shaftesbury, Taunton
50° N	Scilly Isles, Dieppe
01° E	Ashford (Kent), Colchester, North Sea
0°	Brighton, Cambridge, Boston, North Sea
01° W	Portsmouth, Lasham, Reading, Buckingham, Husbands Bosworth, east of Nottingham & York, Middlesbrough
02° W	Poole, Devizes, Cirencester, Evesham, Leek, Skipton, Berwick
03° W	Taunton, east of Talgarth, W of Long Mynd, Lake District, Edinburgh, W of Aboyne
04° W	Plymouth, Snowdon, Galloway, Stirling, Aviemore
05° W	Truro, Milford Haven, Stranraer, Ben Nevis, Cape Wrath
06° W	Dublin, Belfast
07° W	Lough Foyle, Waterford

Summary

Ensure that you understand the following points:

- Importance of NOTAMs
- Contents of NOTAMs
- What to look for in NOTAMs
- How key warnings such as parachute jumps, air displays and royal flights are given.

Questions

1. You want the NOTAMs and permanent changes to airspace. Where do you look?
2. The Red Arrows are performing a display at a village fete on your route. Would you get a good view from your glider?
3. You see a NAV warning containing the abbreviation PJE. What does this mean?
4. A temporary Class A airway has been established. Under what circumstances can you cross it?
5. The date and time on a NOTAM was shown as 08/06/05 09:50 What date and time would you infer from this information?

NAVIGATION

Introduction

Despite the availability of GPS, the art of navigation must still be learned. The GPS signal is not completely reliable, the equipment can fail and it is subject to errors by its operator. Furthermore, not all electronic devices have the latest airspace information, so that a traditional chart and compass must often be used to plot your course. This chapter therefore describes some principles and techniques.

Charts

The BGA states that pilot in charge of a glider may not deliberately undertake a cross-country flight unless he holds a Bronze Badge with cross-country endorsement or higher qualification and carries with him maps marked clearly with the controlled and regulated airspace. The BGA states that carrying a chart is interpreted as being necessary for flights more than 5 nautical miles from your site. Electronic devices do not excuse you from this interpretation. The law also requires adequate equipment necessary for the flight which includes maps and charts for the intended flight including any diversion that might reasonably be expected.

Most pilots just use in a UK is the half-million-scale aeronautical chart. Note that these charts change every year, and you must therefore regularly buy the latest edition. However, even the latest edition of the chart may not show recently announced changes to airspace. Gliding clubs receive detailed amendments to the current charts, and these are also published in the monthly *Supplements to the UK Aeronautical Information Publication*, but a summary can be found by searching for "charts" on NATS web site.

The quarter-million-scale charts do not show the airspace over 5000 feet and above FL55, and often they have too much detail, which can be confusing. However some people find that quarter mil maps are a help in unfamiliar areas, especially if they are looking for a tricky turning point without GPS.

The chart's legend

It is essential that you understand the legend at the base of the chart, and that you are aware of the tables of information. From the previous chapters, you should already be able to identify:

- Airways, control areas and zones, TMAs and their minimum and maximum heights
- Danger, restricted and prohibited areas and their minimum and maximum heights
- Airfields, ATZ and MATZ
- Heights of places on the ground (spot heights) and the heights of airfields and obstructions
- Hazards such as parachute zones, launching winches and gas venting sites
- High Intensity Radio Transmission Areas
- The frequencies of parachute drop zones and airfields
- Normal geographical features such as roads, towns, lakes, rivers and contours

Folding the chart

The half-million chart is 1.25 metres by 1 metre, and so it can easily obscure your view. Unfolding a badly-folded chart in flight is also time-consuming. Before you fly, you should therefore fold it cunningly, so that all the most likely areas for your flights can be seen by a simple unfold or a flip. If you trim the chart, you will lose valuable information at its edges.

For example, for the southern UK map, fold away the English Channel using an east-west fold and then fold the rest of the chart in half using another east-west fold. This ensures that the north and south of your likely flight area are visible on either side of the folded map. Using a north-south fold, firstly fold the map in half and then create a 'concertina' by making a further six alternate north-south folds.

Drawing on your chart

Buy the coated version of the chart, so that you can draw and erase tasks during the year by using an indelible marker. A ruler, calculator, a protractor and meths to erase old lines will complete your kit.

Always draw the route on the chart. It takes a surprisingly long time to find your supposed position on a chart otherwise. The lines will direct your eyes to where you should be looking. As you

Navigation

fly, you will also be able to compare your actual position with the planned track. Note your planned heading on each leg, but do not write on key features.

The lines that you draw are essential to plan your course past airspace and other hazards. Make a careful note of maximum and minimum heights at each airspace boundary. You should be flying with your altimeter set to QNH most of the time, though at times it may be set to 1013. (See *Altitude* chapter.)

Turn-points

The planning of your badge flights (after Silver distance) will include turn-points. With flight recorders, you can either fly within 0.5km of each of your turn-points (cylinder method) or you can fly though a sector at each turn-point. You cannot mix these methods in one flight, but you do not need to decide the method before take-off. Depending on the recording interval, ensure that you spend long enough to record a fix within the zone.

If you use the cylinder method, you merely have to fly to 0.5km of the start, the finish and each turn-point, but note this reduces the distance for the badge by 0.5km at each turn point and at the start and finish. On a triangular task of 301km, the distance flown would be counted as 299km.

The sector method allows you to avoid bad weather or a gaggle over the turn-point, but it is surprisingly easy to miss the sector. It is therefore a good idea to work out in advance what you would expect to see when you are beyond the turn-point.

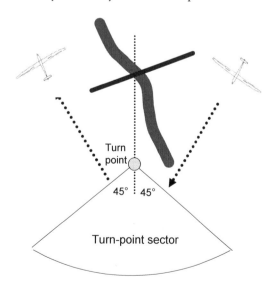

Turn point

45° 45°

Turn-point sector

A GPS will enable you to monitor the heading to the turn point, until it matches the direction of bisector. Alternatively you can choose features from maps or photos that will be visible directly beyond the turn point when you are in the zone. The diagram above illustrates this by depicting how a river-bridge might be oriented when you are truly beyond the turn-point looking down the dotted bisector. There is no limit on the distance beyond the turn-point using the sector method.

Full details about turn-points and badge flights can be found in the Sporting Code
http://www.fai.org/gliding/taxonomy/term/16

Magnetic variation

Magnetic compasses do not point directly to the true geographical North Pole. They point to the Magnetic North Pole instead, which is in the Canadian Arctic. The difference between the bearings to the two poles is called 'magnetic variation'. (Note that maps are always drawn using true north.)

At the time of writing the difference in the UK is no more than about 5° and in most places it is somewhat less. The variation is marked on the half million scale chart as dashed lines (isogonals) that run across the chart and have numbers such as 2.5°W at each end in the margins. (A westerly variation means that magnetic north is to the west of true north.)

The reason for mentioning magnetic variation is that elsewhere in the world it is far greater. For example, in South Africa magnetic variation is up to 23°W, while in New Zealand, it is up to 23°E. In the USA it changes from 4°W in Florida to 15°E in California.

To find the true bearing from a magnetic one and vice versa, the rule is commonly said to be 'variation west, magnetic best; variation east, magnetic least.'

Stated in this way, this rule can be confusing. What it actually means is that in the UK where there is a western variation, the compass will be luring you slightly left towards the Canadian Arctic when you thought you were flying due north. In the UK true north (and all other true bearings) will therefore be slightly to the right of where the compass indicates.

To fly due north, you must therefore fly on a magnetic bearing in the UK of between 03° and 05°. Similarly for all other bearings in the UK, the magnetic bearing will always be greater than the true bearing. Magnetic is therefore bigger and so 'best', and you must always add the western variation on to the true bearing to get the magnetic bearing.

To take another example, a true bearing of due south (180°) in the UK might be typically 183° magnetic.

Conversely, a pilot in New Zealand or California would subtract the local easterly variation to get from true to magnetic. Magnetic would therefore be smaller and so 'least'.

Many books about navigation emphasise this correction for magnetic variation. This is appropriate for powered aircraft because they usually fly at consistent speeds in the same direction. Their pilots can therefore set their courses with great precision in advance.

Gliders do not fly at the same speed and course for long. This is mainly because the location of the best lift is rarely exactly on track. Gliders therefore quickly deviate from the ideal track by amounts that make the corrections for variation in the UK immaterial.

Other compass errors

Among other errors, magnetic compasses are also subject to 'magnetic deviation'. This is caused by metal objects or electrical items within the glider and can be adjusted by small compensating magnets below the compass. Take care if you fit new instruments or a loudspeaker, because your compass may be affected.

You may have a compass card with your glider that gives you the deviation errors in the compass for various magnetic headings. If not, you can estimate your own corrections by pointing the glider in different directions on the ground, and then comparing the heading shown by the compass in the glider with another compass held further away.

At angles of bank of more than 15°, you may find that a basic compass swings about as the glider turns, and as it changes speed, or it may not swing at all. When it swings, it makes it much harder to straighten up on a heading, especially when cloud-flying. In the Northern Hemisphere, the rule when turning onto a heading is: 'undershoot North, overshoot South'. This means that to turn on to a bearing of 360°, straighten out 30° early. To turn on to 180°, straighten up 30° after passing south.

The correction is zero degrees when turning to the east or west, and somewhere in between zero and 30° for the other bearings.

A useful trick if turning before entering cloud is to note the compass bearing when the glider is pointing to the track that you will follow after you leave the cloud.

In the Northern hemisphere, when heading East or West, if you accelerate the compass swings north, and, if you decelerate, the compass swings south. However some gliders are fitted with *Bohli*® compasses, which are not adversely affected by the turning and acceleration of the glider.

Flying a course

Before you attempt a solo cross-country flight, you should fly a navigation exercise with an instructor. In this flight you should be shown how to identify landmarks on the chart from the features on the ground and to fly on the desired headings.

It is surprisingly easy to get a wrong mental picture about your direction, or where landmarks and turn-points are supposed to be. (Many people would swear than Manchester is further west than Edinburgh for example. It isn't.) You may also have a simplistic view of the directions of motorways and railways, and so become disoriented. They snake about the country more than you might realise. You must therefore check your heading regularly by using your compass rather than flying where your instinct tells you.

You should note the time when you flew near a known feature and so when it was that you last knew your exact position. In this way you can later estimate how far you have travelled and in which direction.

Although you should be mainly using your compass, it is also a good idea to know where you would expect to see the sun throughout the flight.

The term 'reciprocal heading' is used for a course in exactly the opposite direction to the present course. To calculate the reciprocal of a heading, add or subtract 180°, whichever is easier to do in your head.

Navigation by landmarks

Before your flight you should identify the major landmarks every 10-15 kilometres on track and on either side of your track. Each landmark on track can usually be seen before the previous landmark disappears from view. Large towns and motorways are best because there is usually only one in the area and so are not easily confused.

However, some features on the chart are not always easy to see. Airfields in particular seem to disappear on the ground, usually because of cloud shadow. Some features such as roads and railways are also too narrow to be easily seen from a great distance; you often have to look hard. You will also quickly find that there is a big difference between the time at which a landmark appears in the distance and the time when you actually reach it.

Parts of the UK (eg the Cotswolds and west of Salisbury) have fewer distinctive features. In these areas you must rely on the compass heading until the next landmark appears. Check your compass heading even more regularly, and be aware when you deviate off course to find lift.

In planning your flight you should have identified the features that will be visible eventually when you emerge from a 'blank area'. Rough calculations (see later) about your speed should tell you when the features will be reached.

It is possible to 'over-navigate', especially if you have a quarter-million scale chart, by identifying every village on the route. It is usually sufficient to know that you are somewhere between two places, unless you are getting near airspace boundaries. However there is a greater risk in 'under-navigating', ie allowing long periods of time to elapse before checking your position.

In fixing your position, try to identify more than one feature, and ideally three, because some features such as towns can easily be confused with each another. Check whether the town has a railway and/or a by-pass running in the right direction; or perhaps a lake/canal/river where you are expecting one. These additional features will help to confirm on the chart what you suspect.

If you think that you have found the place on a ground, make a hypothesis, such as "If this is X I should be able to see on the chart a lake/by-pass/railway to the N/S/E/W of the town. Then look at the map to see if this theory works.

Some distances and times

To estimate your position, it will be helpful to understand how fast you are going. If, for example, you knew your position 15 minutes ago, you should be able estimate how far you have gone since.

British glider pilots use both nautical miles (because we fly with air-speed indicators marked in knots and in winds measured in knots) and kilometres (because our tasks and task speeds are measured this way). You should choose just one of these units and try to stick with it when you are calculating in flight.

On a half-million chart, 1 inch represents 6.85 nautical miles, which can be rounded to 7nm (12.7km), while 10mm represents 5 kilometres. However the handiest measurement is the top joint of your thumb which for me represents about 10 nautical miles or 18.5 kilometres. (You should measure your own.)

Your average-cross country speed (ie both thermalling and gliding) on your early flights may be 50 kph. Assuming no headwind or tailwind, at this speed one thumb would take up to 22 minutes.

A 10 knot headwind will decrease your average cross country speed by up to 10 knots, so a thumb could take about 35 minutes. Conversely for a flight in a 10 knot tailwind, one thumb will take about 16 minutes.

You can see that a wind can make a big difference to your navigation and it is therefore vital that you know about the forecast winds at flying heights before you take off.

Navigating in cross-winds

A cross-wind will blow you off course, reducing your cross-country speed. This is because it effectively increases the distance that you have to fly; even it is blowing exactly at right angles to your course. Your track (ie your course over the ground) will therefore not be the same as your heading (ie where your glider and compass are pointing). Consequently, cross-winds will affect your heading far more than magnetic variation in the UK.

When planning your flight, you can allow for cross-winds when you decide on the headings that you will follow on each leg. It is not realistic to do this calculation while flying. The following example gives a typical calculation, but you are not required to do this in the Bronze Exam.

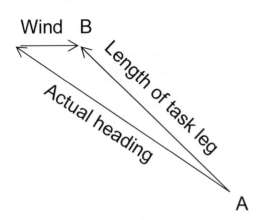

You are flying from A to B. The distance from A to B is 75km. You think your cross country speed would be 65kph on a no-wind day. With no wind the leg would therefore take 75/65 = 1.15hours.

If there is an 8 knot (15kph) wind coming from due west at flying heights, in that time you will have been blown 15 x 1.15 = 17km. You should therefore draw a line that comes from the direction of the wind and that ends at B. It should have a length of 17km/500,000, ie 34mm.

When you complete the triangle with the third line, you can measure the heading of the third line to give you your planned heading. If you apply a speed of 65kph to this effective distance, you will also estimate the time you will take.

If your actual cross-country speed is worse than your prediction, the cross-wind correction will be greater.

What to do if you are lost
There will often be times in any flight when you will not know your exact position. This is not the same as being irretrievably lost. You can usually work out where you are.

The first step is therefore not to panic. Have a good look around, especially directly below and behind in the direction from which you have come. Very often something that you had identified earlier will still be visible.

Using the glider's compass, you can quickly take an approximate bearing. For example if you are pointing at a familiar object and the compass is reading southeast, you are northwest of the object.

You can also work out an approximate distance from an object. At 6,000 feet above the ground, if you look down by 45 degrees, what you see will also be 6,000 feet (about a nautical mile) away.

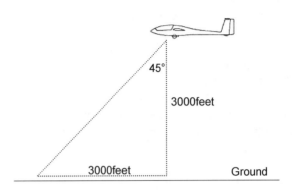

The same rule applies to all other heights. In other words at 3000 feet, by looking down by 45 degrees, you will see objects on the ground about half of a nautical mile away. Using this distance as a unit, you can then very roughly decide how many of these units distant something else is.

If you think you can identify a landmark nearby, see if its features appear on the chart. Towns often have associated railways, roads, rivers and lakes nearby which will help to confirm their identities.

If there is no recognisable landmark, check the bearing on which you have been flying. If you have been following this course since your last known position, you can estimate where you probably are and predict what should appear shortly.

If you are lost near controlled airspace
If you think you are in airspace, the safest decision is to land immediately. Drifting on in the hope that something to turn up will often make the problem worse.

If landing would be hazardous, because you are over a large city or over mountainous terrain, you can call on 121.5MHz, which is the distress frequency. You can quickly find your position from London Centre if you are anywhere in the UK south of 55°N and above 2000 feet. If you are north of this latitude, 3000 feet is needed, and you should ask Scottish Centre on this frequency.

You should first listen to ensure that no other emergency is in progress. The dialogue should begin with an honest statement of the problem:

Navigation

Glider: "London/Scottish Centre, Glider 123 is lost. Request position fix."

You may be asked whether you have a transponder. At the time of writing this is unlikely and so you should answer "Negative". They will take a few minutes to plot your position.

Once two-way communication has been established, do not leave this frequency without telling the controller.

When you return, notify your CFI that you used the emergency service and volunteer for more training in navigation.

It is important to note that the GOTO function on a simple GPS can take a pilot directly through intervening controlled airspace if the pilot is not aware of the glider's position at all times on the paper chart.

Summary
The main points are:
- Get to know the half-million-scale chart
- Fold the chart systematically
- Plan the flight by marking the course, turn-point zones and headings on the chart
- Decide which landmarks will be visible along or near the track
- Check the airspace maxima and minima along and near to your course
- Check your heading frequently when you are flying straight
- Do not guess your heading by instinct, use the compass and chart
- Note the time that you pass over or near recognisable landmarks for future reference
- Look at the features on the ground and then compare them with the chart (not the other way round)
- Recognise that cross-winds will throw you off course and so you should adjust your heading to compensate
- If lost and near airspace, land.

Questions
1. You decide to fly without drawing your route on your chart. What difficulties might you encounter?
2. You see a small town that you do not recognise. What can you do to identify it?
3. What must you carry if you fly more than 5 nautical miles from your launch airfield?
4. You are planning a flight to a turning point 100km due north but there is a 10 knot wind coming from the 315°. You think your cross country speed without a wind would be 65kph. What heading should you fly and how long would it take?
5. You think you may be infringing controlled airspace. What do you do?

LANDING AT ANOTHER AIRFIELD

Introduction
You should already know how to land reliably at your home airfield. This chapter therefore only describes the issues that arise when you land elsewhere. Wherever you land, the basics should not be forgotten: good look-out, proper circuit, the pre-landing checks and speed control.

Landing at another gliding site
A gliding site is usually a better option for landing than a field a few miles further down track. However, there may be complications, so that you would be unwise to plan a flight to another gliding club without getting a specific briefing about the local conditions.

For example there may be other traffic at some gliding airfields, eg Booker, which also has power-flying. Gliders may therefore be subject to special rules, such as circuits being only on one side. There may also be specific local rules about airspace, eg Dunstable, which has a letter of agreement with Luton Airport. Another example is Weston-on-the-Green, which is in a danger area because of parachuting. There may be other hazards which you have not encountered before. For example, Lasham has occasional movements of jet airliners.

If, while flying, you find that you are getting low near another gliding site, you should take the following precautions before landing:
- Do not over-fly the airfield. They may be winch-launching
- Try to identify where the winch cables lie on the ground, and land well to the side of these
- Note the circuit direction and the landing area of other gliders
- In the absence of other gliders, look for the windsock
- Keep a good look-out for other gliders flying locally
- If you know the local frequency, call to ask for information
- If landing on grass, select a mown area.

Landing at a non-gliding airfield
Common questions are 'Can I land at the airfield at XYZ?' and 'Can I land at any unknown airfield?' The simple answer to both questions is that, if you are saving your glider or preventing injury to yourself, you can land anywhere. However, the reception that you get after landing can vary greatly.

The main factor that will determine your welcome will be whether you alerted the airfield before landing. A simple radio call explaining your predicament will enable the airfield to accommodate you.

Some airfields, including all military airfields, are known as 'prior permission only (PPR)'. This means that if you know that you are going to fly there, you should call them up by 'phone before you take off. Again a radio call will help for an unplanned arrival. Small airstrips which are not listed in AIP are by default PPR, though an unplanned landing by a glider is usually treated with understanding.

However if you flagrantly contravene controlled airspace and/or NOTAMs, you might get a fine (in multiple thousands of pounds). At a major civil airport you can also expect a hefty landing-fee.

Some airfields have an ATZ, which you should treat as controlled airspace. If the ATC has air traffic control, then you must get permission to enter. If there is a flight information unit or an air / ground radio station, you should get information to judge whether it is safe to fly within the ATZ. Call up before entering the ATZ to alert them of your height and position even if just flying through, not just before landing. You must then listen in to their frequency and tell them when you leave. AIP gives their hours of operation. Do not fly over any airfield with the symbol for a parachute drop zone.

If you cannot identify the airfield from the air, then landing is risky. You will not be able to call them up in advance, and so you will be unaware of other traffic and other hazards. Small airstrips are relatively safe for unexpected arrivals, but unexpected traffic appearing at a busy airfield risks collision. It is therefore unwise to land at an unknown airfield, unless there is no other safe farmer's field nearby.

Landing at another airfield

You must also seek permission before summoning a tug to retrieve you from another airfield. This is because there are often restrictions placed on airfields, such as insurance, military rules and noise limitations.

Runways

Runways are referred to by their first 2 digits, thus runway direction of 240° magnetic would be referred to as 24.

Calling up another airfield

If it has a frequency, you should if possible call up your intended airfield to get landing information. This will assist you as well as improving everyone else's safety.

A list of the frequencies of airfields is given on the half-million-scale chart. How you address the airfield and how it can reply will depend on its status. The listed airfields have one of the following statuses:

- ATC (Air Traffic Control) – highly important
- AFIS (Aerodrome Flight Information Service) – very important
- A/G (Air to Ground) – important

An ATC will describe itself as "Tower", "Radar", "Approach" or "Control", eg Coventry Tower. ATCs give clearances, which must be followed and repeated back to them.

An AFIS will describe itself as 'Information' eg Goodwood Information. It cannot give instructions such as clearances. It can only give information, and will say 'Land at your discretion'. Repeating the information is not mandatory but helps to confirm the essentials of what you heard.

An Air to Ground airfield will describe itself as 'Radio' eg Old Sarum Radio. They will also give information, but cannot even say 'Land at your discretion'. Again it can help to repeat the information that you are given.

A typical dialogue with a small airfield follows:

Glider: "Old Sarum Radio, Glider Charlie Alpha Bravo Charlie"
A/G: "Bravo Charlie, pass your message"
Glider: "Bravo Charlie is one mile to the south at 800 feet, request joining information"

A/G "Left hand circuit, runway 240, surface Wind 260/10, QNH 1015, QFE 1007. Two aircraft currently in circuit."
Glider: "Roger. Left hand circuit, runway 240. Other aircraft in sight."
Glider: "Bravo Charlie downwind."
Glider: "Bravo Charlie base leg"
Glider: "Bravo Charlie final"

If you call on the correct frequency, but do not get a reply, continue with the circuit, and still make your downwind, base & final calls, ie transmit blind, eg "Bravo Charlie downwind, runway 240, left hand circuit" and later "Bravo Charlie base leg for runway 240" and "Bravo Charlie final for runway 240". There may not be anyone on the ground but other aircraft in the circuit would hear you.

Safetycom

The CAA has defined a radio frequency for use at aerodromes and airstrips in the UK where there is no specific VHF frequency. This frequency is 135.475 MHz and is known as 'Safetycom'.

Where to land

You should comply with the radioed instructions/information and the airfield signs. If in doubt, all turns, including the circuit, should be to the left. If there were no radioed instructions, look for the windsock.

Note that powered aircraft often fly bigger circuits with less steep approaches than gliders, so look downwind in particular when on your base leg for other traffic.

In the absence of instructions, the safest place to land a glider at an active airfield is on a concrete runway, provided that it is clear of other aircraft. The second choice is mown grass. The grass at airfields is not always 'landable' and the borders between the grass and concrete may not be smooth. It is better to risk inconvenience to other users, than to risk running into a hidden pothole or lump of concrete on your ground run. Consequently, if you have not been able to talk on the radio, land on the runway, taxi as far up the runway as possible and turn off to the left. If you stop on the runway, immediately pull the glider off to one side to clear the runway for the next user.

Try to taxi off at a runway intersection. Do not taxi off the runway edges, which may be rough or have lights or disused light-sockets just big enough to swallow a glider's wheel.

If you land at a small private airstrip, it is particularly important to move the glider out of the way in case someone else, such as the owner, also wishes to land. You will be extremely unpopular if you block a small airstrip with your glider.

Disused airfields

The half-million-scale chart shows disused airfields as a circle containing a diagonal cross. These airfields may have only recently been in use, or they may now have a very different use and are totally unsuitable for landing.

Examples of uses of disused airfields (apart from agriculture) are car storage and testing, armament storage, fire brigade training, car-boot sales, industrial parks and army training.

Welford's armaments store (northwest of Newbury) is an example of a disused airfield where you will definitely not be welcome.

It is simplest to say that all disused airfields should be treated with great caution. At best you may find yourself behind locked gates, and at worst you may land on holes or concrete blocks hidden in the grass. The runways on some airfields are very uneven or are obstructed with fences or power cables.

Light signals

You may never see light signals in your gliding career, but you must be aware of what they mean. Basically, any red lights or red flares are warnings to stay away.

- If you are near an airfield and you see RED FLASHES, you are being warned NOT to land there. The signallers will have a good reason and it is dangerous to ignore them.

- A CONTINUOUS RED LIGHT or a red flare is similar to red flashes because they also mean that you must NOT land and must continue circling and giving way to other aircraft. However they may give you permission eventually. Since you are likely

to be running out of height fast, do not count on this.

- GREEN FLASHES are a signal to return to the airfield, but you should still wait for permission to land.

- A CONTINUOUS GREEN LIGHT is the only signal that means that you may land.

- WHITE FLASHES mean that you can land eventually, but only after getting the green light.

The fact that the airfield is busy enough to have people available to shine lights or fire flares probably means that you should have contacted them by radio.

Light signals also have meanings on the ground. Though unpowered gliders have limited taxiing abilities, these signals also apply to vehicles towing gliders. A red light means stop, and red flashes are a signal for you to move clear of the landing area. Green flashes mean that you can move. White flashes are a signal to return to the starting point.

Other airfield signals

Less dramatic than the lights and flares are the signs at smaller airfields that provide useful information to aircraft that do not have radios. Glider pilots, who are considering landing, may have limited time to look for these, but you should be aware of the main signals nevertheless.

The signals can be seen in a 12 metre square area, usually near the control tower. The following are the most important signals.

Circuits are normally left-handed, and so no signal is displayed. However if right-hand circuits are in force, a yellow and red striped arrow should be shown in the signal square.

The T in the signal square shows the direction of landing and take-off along the shaft of the T and towards the cross arm

Landing at another airfield

White dumb-bell with black bars means land on paved surfaces only. If there are no black bars, all ground movements on must be on paved surfaces.

A yellow diagonal cross in a red square means that the airfield is unsafe and that landing is prohibited.

The following ground signs may be seen at other places outside the signals square:

A white diagonal cross on a runway means that this part of the airfield is closed. This runway marking shows that runway 20 is closed.

This marking on the field shows an area that should only be used for the taking-off and landing of gliders

Landing near other aircraft

If you land behind another aircraft, especially a powered aircraft, it is more likely to turn left on the ground. You should therefore land to the right of it, if you are going to taxi alongside.

Severe wake turbulence occurs from the vortices shed from the wing-tips of large aircraft. This turbulence can last a minute after a recent take-off or landing. The turbulence is strongest as the aircraft rotates into the climb at take-off or as it flares to land. Consequently, you should aim to land alongside where the aircraft has been going slowest. If you are landing in the same direction as the other aircraft's movement, you should land long after another aircraft has landed to over-fly the turbulence, and land short after a take-off.

If space permits, landing as far to the side as possible also reduces your risks of encountering a

vortex, and in a cross-wind the upwind side would be slightly better.

Summary

The following points should be understood:

- Hazards at other gliding sites
- Importance of an ATZ
- How to ask for landing information
- Where to land in the absence of radio communication
- Hazards of disused airfields
- Light signals
- Aerodrome signal squares and signs
- Landing with other aircraft.
- Wake turbulence

In all the excitement do not forget to lower your undercarriage and monitor your approach speed.

Questions

1. On arrival at a strange airfield you call on the notified frequency, but get no reply. Your radio is serviceable, what should your actions be?
2. You decide to land beside another aircraft that has just landed. On which side should you pass?
3. You are circling low near an unknown airfield and you see a red flare. Guy Fawkes' Night is not imminent. Is any action needed?
4. You see the signal square at an airfield and it contains a large white T. What does this signify?
5. You have identified the airfield of flying club. You have a radio and you would like to land there, unless things improve quickly. What should you say after establishing contact?
6. You land at a small airstrip. What should your first action be after stopping?
7. You want to land at an airfield immediately after a large jet has landed. Where should you land?

FIELD LANDINGS

Introduction

Landing in a field is a routine event for a cross-country pilot. It is inconvenient, but it need not be feared. With a good choice of field AND a good circuit, safe landings can regularly be made with little risk. This chapter describes the techniques in more detail.

The commonest error

The commonest error in field landings is a late decision to land. You have not irrevocably decided to land if you are still hoping that some lift will appear. Your decision must therefore be final.

You may also be caught in two minds about which is your preferred field. A firm decision to land has only been made if you have also chosen the field.

The late decision usually results in a poor circuit and all the problems that can result from this. The next section therefore considers the heights at which you should have made your decisions.

Decision heights for field landing

Your altimeter will not give your height above the ground. You must be able to judge height by eye. On your next local flights, try to remember what the following decision heights look like.

Choosing a field begins long before you have given up looking for lift. Over flat terrain in the UK at about 2000 feet AGL, look at the terrain ahead and decide if it contains any likely fields. (Elsewhere in the world you might have to fly over worse terrain and so you may need to be much higher.) Some areas may be unpromising because they contain nothing but occupied, small or steep fields. If so, move in a direction that contains better fields, and better lift. Any slopes in any direction that are visible at this height are far too steep to land on. Remember that even if your present location does not have good lift, you still have the height to fly many kilometres to somewhere better.

By 1500 feet AGL, you should be looking at an area with some potential fields. You still have plenty of time to choose the field, while being alert to any lift that may appear in the locality. Note the compass direction of the wind and its direction relative to the sun.

If no field has appeared by now, flying down-wind will enable you to cover more ground in your search.

By 1000 feet AGL, you should have chosen your field, and by 800 feet you should have started your downwind leg. If you encounter lift below 800 feet on the downwind leg, you should ignore it. You are now committed to landing in your chosen field. (Remember all these heights are judged by eye.)

Field selection

Six attributes are important. They have the initial letters WSSSSO:

- Wind
- Size
- Slope
- Surface
- Stock
- Obstructions

It is vital that you have sessions in a motor-glider in which you can use these attributes to assess many fields. However, the following sections give some guidance.

Wind

You should have been aware of the forecast wind, but you can also deduce the current wind direction by using various clues such as smoke and your drift when you were circling.

You can also use cloud shadows to deduce the wind direction. Note that the wind at cloud-base veers by about 30° from the direction at ground level, though a 30° error in estimating the wind direction is usually not serious.

Checking on the orientation of the wind can be done while you are quite high and still looking for the preferred area for your field. Be aware of the effect of sea-breeze fronts and of thunderstorms on the forecast wind-strength and direction (see *Weather* chapter).

Field landings

10 knots of wind is significant if you land downwind, because you may need a landing run that is 200 metres longer than for an into-wind landing. It is therefore important to think about the wind when planning your circuit.

You should be able to cope with a 10 knot cross-wind, but be aware of turbulence from buildings and trees on the up-wind side.

However, if the wind direction seems incompatible with the slope of your preferred field, always choose a downwind landing in preference to a downhill landing.

Size

Choose the biggest field available. The size should be at least 250 metres from where you round out, but try to find a much longer field, if at all possible. You are unlikely to round out right over the field's boundary because you will want to clear fences, hedges, trees or houses. To judge the size of fields, look at the landing area at your home airfield from the circuit, and then after landing, pace out your ground-run.

A working wheel-brake is essential in minimising the ground run. (A glider is unserviceable unless its wheel-brake is working.)

The potential landing run is greatest along the diagonal. If the slope, obstructions, furrows and the wind permit, you should try to use this extra distance (40% longer for a square field).

Slope

The slope is another vital consideration. On any noticeable down-slope, the ground will fall away rapidly below you as you land. Even if you make contact, you will not be able to stop before the far boundary. You must, therefore, avoid all down-slopes.

Landing, across a slope is not recommended because you have to land with banked wings. This means that as you round out after a straight approach, you will turn downhill.

To land across a slope you would have to start from the downhill side, and fly a curved approach so that the amount of bank, as you round out, just points you up the slope. This is a very tricky manoeuvre.

Landing uphill is possible, though it also has its problems (see the special section on this later), but any other slope that is visible from 1000 feet other than an up-slope, is unacceptable.

It is not possible to see the slope of a field, if you only look down at it from directly above. You should look at your field from two sides. Looking for slopes in the circuit will therefore be too late. Be aware that rivers and lakes are always at the bottom of a hill. Landing towards water is, therefore, often a problem.

Surface

The field's surface is another key attribute. You should choose a surface that is not only safe, but one that also causes the least inconvenience to the farmer.

You can safely land in many crops in the early spring, but they become riskier within a few weeks as they get taller. This is because of the danger of catching a wing-tip and ground-looping, or of catching a low tail-plane. Farmers also become upset by a glider landing when the crop is more mature. Retrieving the glider from the midst of tall crop also requires several strong helpers to carry out each component.

Probably the worst crop to land in is oil-seed rape (canola). This is thickly matted from an early stage and has very tough stems. It is hazardous for landing even before it has turned yellow in April, and even after it has been cut.

You should become aware of the state of the crops as you drive about the country throughout the year.

Ploughed fields can break your undercarriage unless you land along the furrows. If you land in crop you should also land along the 'tram-lines' that have been caused by machinery. The wheel-ruts from farm machinery can often be deep enough to break the undercarriage. Always land in the same direction as the wheel-tracks, even in stubble fields.

In some parts of the country, there are ancient ridges and furrows with a depth of over a metre and with 10 metre spacing. These are impossible to land across safely.

The best fields to choose are usually fields where the grass has just been cut for silage or hay, and, from mid-July, stubble fields. Pasture fields tend to be smaller than silage fields, and if they are not smaller, they can be divided by electric fences. Set-aside fields were often useful, but they only had to be cut three times a year, and so could be quite long at times. However set-aside is increasingly rare these days.

Note that playing fields often have goal posts only 100 metres apart (not to mention players). Golf courses are also well populated by golfers.

From mid-June to mid-July, there may be few landable fields. Novice pilots should not attempt cross-countries in these conditions.

Stock

There is at least one circumstance where your insurance may not cover your liability for damage. This is if you injure a valuable race-horse. Race-horses are extremely neurotic and can bolt. A frightened mare might easily miscarry a multi-million pound foal. Consequently, racing stables and stud farms are very unfriendly and must be avoided. Look out for the wooden fencing used by stud farms rather than wire used for other livestock.

Other livestock is less valuable, but you should also steer clear. Cattle, sheep and pigs are substantial objects that will damage your glider if you collide, and, in the case of cattle, may damage you. Even if you miss the cattle, you will discover that they are still a problem. Until it can be rescued, you will have to defend your glider from the curiosity and the strange appetites of cattle.

Obstructions

The size of field required is greatly affected by the height of the obstructions that you must clear on the downwind boundary. Trees, houses or telephone wires will mean that you do not round out at the edge, but a long way into the field. For example, if you just clear a 15 metre tree, you will round out further into the field by at least ten times this height, ie over 150 metres into the field. If you thought that the field was only just long enough to begin with, you may not be able to stop in time before the far boundary.

Be wary of poles running along the boundary of a field or across a field. These poles probably carry power or telephone cables, which are usually invisible from the air. A solitary pole should be a great concern, because you may be unable to see the direction of the cables.

Trees on the downwind boundary, as well as causing clearance problems may also generate turbulence as you approach.

Fences

Electric fences and post-and-wire fences are often difficult to see from the air. Electric fences are used to divide up large pastures so that the grass is grazed systematically. They can sometimes be spotted by the change in colour of the grass, or by a water trough that straddles the line of the fence.

If you are just rounding out, and you see a fence immediately ahead, a useful trick is to close the airbrakes completely. The glider will rise by about six feet and glide a considerable distance. Land again as if you had 'ballooned'. You can practise this at your home airfield.

Other considerations

Other considerations in your choice of field are relatively minor. For example, landing near a housing estate may attract some unwelcome curiosity, and could encourage onlookers into the field.

Once you have the circuit under control, noticing the direction of the farm-house and road access may save you a long walk. However, this should not be a factor in your field selection.

The circuit

A good circuit into a field is better than a poor circuit into a larger field. Be careful therefore about any last minute changes of mind about the preferred field. These can seriously disrupt your circuit.

The techniques that you learned to make accurate landings at your home airfield still apply. You were not taught these merely to please the instructors. Do not forget the normal pre-landing checks, including tightening your straps and lowering the undercarriage.

The only sure way to touch down at the desired point at a controlled speed is to do a final turn about two fields back (assuming light winds) from the downwind boundary of the field. You then have a chance of stabilising the direction, the speed and the rate of descent.

The only sure way to get to the final turn at the right height is by doing a standard circuit. There is a tendency to want to look closely at the chosen field, so that the pilot is tempted to fly directly above it. Instead, you must do a proper circuit to allow you to make the adjustments that will get you to the final turn at the right height. Your downwind leg should be the distance of two average-sized fields out to the side.

If you get too close to the field on the downwind leg, it will quickly disappear behind you, well before the base leg should start. As a result, you will not know when to turn on to your base leg. If you turn too early, the downwind boundary of your field will be almost directly beneath you. You will be too high and have little time to stabilise your speed and direction. Your chances of a safe landing will now be considerably reduced.

When landing in a field, good speed control is essential. 5 extra knots of approach speed can add 100 metres of ground run on a firm field, but you must also not be too slow. Accuracy of speed control can only be reliably achieved by a long approach, which in turn can only be achieved by a good circuit. Half to two-thirds airbrake will give you more options as you approach. Do not be so distracted by the field that you do not look at the ASI.

As ever, touch down at minimum speed, ie a fully held-off landing. Any excess speed could project you upwards, if you hit a bump. After touching down, apply full airbrake. Apply wheel-brake, but not so much as to lift the glider off its tail-wheel.

An ability to side-slip at a moment's notice can transform an excessively high approach into a safe landing. However, do not attempt a sideslip unless you are in good practice. A badly executed sideslip can make matters worse. You should therefore practice full airbrake sideslips at your home airfield, after getting instruction.

Landing uphill

If you have chosen an uphill field, you must be aware of the optical illusion that you will experience. You will instinctively imagine that the field is flat, and so adjust the attitude of the glider to make the approach look normal.

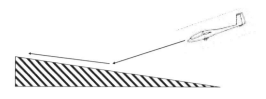

The approach to an up-slope looks steeper and you have to round out more.

An up-slope gives the impression of a steeper approach. You may, therefore, feel that you want to reduce the apparent angle by reducing your speed. Instead, you need even more speed than usual, because the glider has to round out even further in order to fly up the slope.

An approach speed of 65 knots, and even 70 knots for steep up-slopes, should therefore be maintained if you are landing on an up-slope, especially if you are landing into wind because there may be curl-over. You should also round out sooner than normal because you have to raise the nose further. When landing uphill, the glider will slow up quickly when rounding out and when on the ground run, even with a high approach speed.

After you stop, you may have to use the wheel brake to stop the glider rolling back.

If it all goes wrong

The glider is a minor consideration when you are about to have an accident. If an obstruction is very close, put a wing down to make the glider ground-loop. Expect to break the fuselage near the tail at least. Even if no damage is apparent, get the glider inspected.

If you encounter a wire fence, do not expect that you will simply demolish it by ploughing through. The wire can slice through the canopy. Again a ground-loop can be considered.

If you are landing in tall crop, try to hold off for as long as possible, stall just above the crop and keep the wings level. Closing the airbrakes may prevent the lower paddles catching in the crop and stopping the wings abruptly.

If you are landing on a rock-pile, sideslip in so that a wing takes the full impact.

Landing on water

Although landing on water is unlikely to be necessary in agricultural areas, forests and mountains could leave a glider pilot with no option but to choose a lake. (Streams may have steep sides and may be strewn with rocks; they are unlikely to be a good choice.) There were ten water landings in Sweden over a period of fifteen years and none resulted in serious injury or damage.

Call on the radio and then turn off the electrics. Locate canopy jettison lever. Land at the minimum speed with the undercarriage down. Land parallel to and close to a windward shore in deep water. Similarly at sea, your tactic should be to land along the waves near the shore. Close airbrakes before touching down if possible. Because the glider's canopy may break because of the sudden pressure of water, shield your eyes just before touch-down.

After landing the glider will be blown into the shore and this will reduce the depth and distance from which the glider must be retrieved. The glider will float because of the amount of air in the wings so you have time to think. Do not try swimming fully clothed.

After landing

Secure the glider and report to the club that you are safe. Try to track down the land-owner or a representative. Find out exactly where you are to arrange the retrieve.

Distress & Diversion Cell of NATS has requested that pilots should let them know if they have landed out and have to leave the glider in the field overnight or if, for any reason, they believe that the land-out has caused or is likely to cause alarm. In these events, you should call the D&D Cell

- London D&D: 01895-426150
- Scottish D&D: 01292-692380

letting them know the location and confirming that there are no casualties.

Dealing with the farmer

You are an uninvited guest, so be apologetic for inconveniencing the farmer. Pay for any phone calls.

If you are asked for payment, do not immediately dismiss the idea. Explain that any damage will be settled by your insurance company. Emphasise that the landing was an unplanned emergency (unlike balloonists). If money is still requested, pay up

gracefully, though you might suggest the cheque is payable to a local charity. Bear in mind that you may still need the farmer's help to get out of the field.

You need the farmer's permission to bring the trailer on to the field, because the car and trailer can do much more damage than the glider and its pilot. You may also need gates to be unlocked.

If you have caused damage, some reassurance can be provided by having your insurance details to hand and giving these to the farmer. Contact your broker immediately if a claim is being made. Take photographs and make notes of the damage.

The farmer is not entitled to detain your glider. If this is attempted, you should point out that the farmer is taking responsibility for the safe-keeping of valuable and delicate equipment. If this explanation is unsuccessful in releasing the glider, call the police. As a last resort, your insurers will obtain an injunction to release the glider, if necessary.

Take a note of the farmer's name and address for a thank-you letter, an air-experience flight and/or an invitation to the annual farmers' party at your club.

Giving directions

It is usually better to meet your crew at an easily identifiable junction or a village. Small farm tracks are not well sign-posted and three-point turns with a trailer are stressful. Some advance planning of the best way into the field with a trailer will also be appreciated.

Do not drive on any field without permission. If the farmer was not contacted, push the glider to the gate and carry out the components to the trailer.

Be aware that the hot catalytic converter on a car's exhaust can ignite a stubble field. A fire started this way quickly spread and consumed a glider.

Aero-towing from fields

Aero-towing out of a field requires a skilled tug-pilot, a powerful tug and a long, firm field, plus the permission of the land-owner. You need about 800 metres of field with no up-slope and no obstructions as you climb away. Pace out the field to confirm its length. If the tug-pilot does not like the look of the field, you will still be liable for the cost of the abortive trip by the tug.

Field landings

Summary

The main points are:

- There will be times when there are insufficient landable fields for novice pilots to attempt cross-countries
- Make an timely and irrevocable decision to land
- Select the field by wind, size, slope, surface, stock and obstructions
- Never land downhill
- Obstructions on the approach massively reduce the usable length of the field
- The circuit should be as wide as normal – about two fields out to the side and two fields back in light winds
- The speed control should be accurate
- You are more valuable than the glider
- Be polite, considerate and apologetic to farmers.
- Ensure that you have a working wheel-brake.

Questions

1. What are the six main factors that should determine your choice of field?
2. The normal approach speed of your glider is 55 knots in still air and your landing run is normally 250 metres. You have chosen a flat field that is 700 metres long and you will approach at 60 knots over a 20 metre tree with a 10 knot tail-wind. How far into the field will you stop from the tree?
3. You decide to land on an up-slope, what effect will this have on your approach speed and round-out?
4. You have a good look at your field from almost above as you start your downwind leg. What effect may this have on your landing?
5. At what height above your chosen field would you reject a potential thermal?

HUMAN FACTORS

Introduction

A good understanding of human behaviour and physiology is important in flying safely. Though most accidents are caused by pilot error, many of these have more complex causes than just plain stupidity. This chapter describes these factors and some of the associated laws and rules. The factors have been grouped into:

- Fitness to fly
- Psychology
- Physiology

FITNESS TO FLY

Age

A degree of maturity is needed to fly in a glider. In particular a trainee should be able to receive and comply with instructions. There is no legal lower limit but considerations about ballast often put the lower limit for flying dual at 12 years old. The minimum age for solo flight is 16.

There is no maximum age for flying a glider, but some pilots may show reduced mental and physical fitness as they grow older. They should adjust the level of their flying to take account of this.

Medicals

Before your first flight with an instructor you should have signed a form that simply declared you were fit enough for a dual flight. However to fly solo, the self-declaration form has to be endorsed by the pilot's doctor. This self-declaration remains valid until age 45, at which time a new self-declaration must be made and endorsed by the pilot's own doctor. Self-declarations must then be renewed (with a doctor's endorsement) at ages 50, 55, 60, and 65, then annually. It is recommended that the self-declarations are made in the month that they expire. If you have had a serious illness, a new declaration is required.

It is the responsibility of the pilot (not the gliding club) to check that his medical is in date.

Full details of the medical requirements are on the BGA web site:
http://www.gliding.co.uk/bgainfo/medical.htm

If your driving licence has been revoked on medical grounds, you automatically become unfit to fly gliders solo.

Your physical well-being

There can be several reasons why you could be feeling below par. Each of these can significantly reduce your ability to fly a glider. These reasons include:

- Illness
- Medication
- Stress
- Alcohol
- Fatigue
- Flying currency
- Eating

The initial letters of these factors spell out (rather badly) I'M SAFE. Each factor is described in more detail in the following sections.

Illness

Some people may try to fly with minor illnesses such as a slight headache, food poisoning, blocked sinuses or a blocked nose. These can reduce concentration severely. Apart from the distraction, flying with a blocked nose can damage your hearing and can lead to worse infections (see the *Ears* section later). Decongestants are only partly effective. <u>Do not fly with a cold</u>.

Medication and drugs

Some medication can produce sleepiness, dizziness or other reactions that will affect your concentration. Be aware of the effect of any treatment, such as anti-histamines and inoculations. If in doubt, seek medical advice or read the instruction leaflet provided with the medicine. (Illicit drugs are totally incompatible with aviation.)

You should not fly for 24 hours after a local anaesthetic, for example at your dentist, and 48 hours after a general anaesthetic.

Donating blood should also debar you from flying for at least 24 hours. Flying high even after waiting a day after giving blood is likely to be risky. (The RAF ban after blood donation is for seven days.)

Human factors

Mental stress and other distractions

Mental stress can arise from many causes and will reduce your concentration greatly. It could be from an argument, difficulty at work, debt, general depression, illness in the family, being late to launch, annoyance with inefficiency at the launch point, being hurried up before you launch, or any sudden shock. Be aware that you are wound up. Do not fly until you have calmed down.

Women are affected by their menstrual cycle to differing degrees, and individually must decide when they are fit to fly.

Annoyances in flight such as a constant whine, hum or hiss can increase your stress greatly. You may even be unaware of what is driving you mad until you switch it off.

Be wary of any distraction in flight. Interesting sights on the ground, a dropped sandwich or leakages during urination are examples of events which will divert attention from the main task in hand.

Alcohol

Alcohol is a quickly acting depressant for the central nervous system. Although skill is adversely affected by alcohol equivalent to only a pint of bitter, judgment is affected by even lower levels of alcohol and, as a result, higher risks than normal are accepted.

The Railways and Transport Safety Act sets the alcohol limit that applies to gliding at 20mg/100ml, which is one quarter of the level for car drivers, but even this seems lax for flying gliders. This limit applies to anyone involved in flying operations, even a wing-tip holder. Note that the effects of alcohol are doubled at 10,000 feet. You should therefore wait at least eight hours before flying if you have consumed a small amount of alcohol.

It takes about an hour to eliminate 1 unit of alcohol from the blood. (Half a pint of bitter is one unit.) Consequently on the morning after a binge, some motorists have even failed a police breath test. The old RAF rule about eight hours 'from bottle to throttle' only ever applied to a very modest amount of alcohol. The RAF now requires 24 hours of abstinence before flying.

The quantity of food that you eat at the same time affects the rate at which your absorb alcohol but it is all absorbed eventually. Exercise, sleep and coffee have no effect on the rate at which you eliminate alcohol. Recent studies have shown that fluids in the balance organs in the ears will retain alcohol for several days after it has been flushed from the blood stream.

You will also find that you sleep better if you have not drunk alcohol, so that you will be more alert when you fly the next day. You will also not start the day dehydrated if you have abstained (see later).

Fatigue

Getting a good night's sleep before flying is essential. After a bad night you will often feel reasonably wide awake in the morning, especially if busy, but severe fatigue may occur later in the day. Do not work late and try to relax long before retiring to bed. Avoid caffeine (tea or coffee) for six hours before bed-time. Severe jet-lag should ground you.

Fatigue can also arise from excessive flying. You may have had a long struggle to stay airborne or you may have had many launches on that day already. Be aware that your concentration is beginning to wander. Stop flying, if fatigued.

Some pilots have even taken the courageous decision to withdraw part way through a competition because of fatigue. It may be relevant that several accidents involving very experienced pilots have happened in competitions.

Boredom can also induce fatigue. In particular, pilots are often not concentrating well throughout an attempted Silver duration flight. Every flight should have a purpose, so do not fly aimlessly. For example, try setting some local triangles, and then timing your speed on each circuit.

Flying currency

It is noticeable that if you fly on several consecutive days, all turns suddenly become well-co-ordinated, speed control on the approach becomes rock steady and all decisions become easier to take. However, many pilots rarely get to this state even in the height of summer.

Flying occasionally, perhaps staying just within the club's currency rules for a long period is dangerous. Rustiness makes you far less capable of efficiently dealing with even minor problems. If you are feeling out of practice, get a check flight, or preferably even more than one.

A pilot may be current at routine circuits but may easily not be current on winching, stalling, spinning, launch failures or landing out: in fact the main things that hurt people in gliding. For this reason when deciding if a pilot is current, not just total hours and launches be considered and but also how recent launch failure, stalls and spins have been experienced. Pilots learn and subsequently forget at different rates therefore how long a pilot can go without flying a glider varies enormously. Much depends on the pilot's experience, the difficulty of the site, weather, the purpose of the flight and the pilot's well-being, both physical and mental.

The BGA suggests that pilots who are inexperienced at cross country flying should have as a minimum annual field landing training. With experience, the frequency of training flights can be extended and included within the routine refresher training cycle.

It is now mandatory for all pilots who fly British registered aircraft to keep a log book. It is also useful in reminding you when you last flew or landed in a field.

Eating

Diabetics will already be aware of the need to maintain blood sugar levels. Non-diabetics may not be aware that a reduction in your blood sugar levels will cause you not only to feel hungry, but will seriously reduce your alertness. Hunger and fatigue are a particularly dangerous combination.

Consequently, you should never skip breakfast or lunch and then fly. Fly with snacks, though those made of pure sugar produce only a short term fix followed by a 'crash' in blood sugar. More complex foods such as sandwiches and fruit provide energy over a longer period.

Getting comfortable

An uncomfortable pilot will not be able to concentrate. It is therefore worth spending time and money to ensure that you can stay comfortable for hours. A specially moulded support was made to fit between one pilot's back and his parachute. (See *Sailplane & Gliding Vol 53 Issue 6 Page 28*)

If you accept a seating position that is too low in the cockpit, the landing area under the nose of the glider will not be visible. Proper support should therefore be installed.

Do not use soft cushions to improve your comfort. These are positively dangerous. Firstly, they will compress in high g, and so you will be forced lower in your seat, and possibly out of reach of the controls. Secondly, in an accident they will not offer any resistance to the impact. You will hit the seat as if you had been suspended a few inches above it. This may produce worse injuries than if you had been firmly in contact with the seat.

However there should be a seat cushion because additional protection is needed in case of a heavy landing. It should be made of energy absorbing material such as *Confor®*, and should be well secured to the glider to stop it slipping in flight. If the cushion were to slip forward, it would restrict the backward movement of the stick.

A short pilot may need to be moved forward in the cockpit to enable him to exert full control movements. If so, firm packing should be placed behind the pilot's back. This is particularly important in the first stages of a winch-launch. Firm-grade chip-foam is a cheap and suitable material for seat backs, but it is not energy absorbing, and so it should not be used to sit on.

Urination

The lower temperatures, stress and the water that you already should be drinking will make you produce urine while flying. You will not be able to concentrate properly with a full bladder, so be sure to take your chosen method to urinate in flight. This activity should not require so much attention that your look-out suffers.

Caffeine from tea or coffee can accelerate dehydration by increasing production of urine, so you might prefer something else with your breakfast.

Pregnancy

Consult your doctor, but expect that pregnancy will prevent flying for at least the first three months and the last three months of the term. After nine months, other constraints may apply!

PSYCHOLOGY

The following sections describe a group of factors affecting your state of mind when you fly.

Minimising work-load

Check lists, recent flying experience, mnemonics and a general systematic approach to gliding reduce work-load and free up brain-power for the non-routine aspects and help to overcome distractions. It is also better to write information down for use in flight rather than using your memory.

Your decisions will be far quicker if you have mentally rehearsed emergencies. Cable breaks are the most common emergency to anticipate, but have you also thought about which straps you would unbuckle, and which knobs you would pull to bale out?

One pilot who thought he was adjusting the rudder pedals at 50 feet, pulled off an aero-tow unexpectedly. He could have minimised his workload by getting comfortable before take-off.

Think through other points in your flight in advance, such as how you would make your decision to land in a field, and when to abort a low final-glide.

Be aware that some controls can be confused at times of stress. The most common confusions are between the flaps, air-brakes and/or undercarriage. Re-familiarise yourself with all controls before you take-off and before you need to use them in a hurry. Being too busy can have serious consequences when preparing an aircraft for flight. In particular, a distraction while rigging can mean your controls are not connected. (Once, a pilot successfully flew a circuit in a glider with no main pin to hold the wings together, but you might not be so lucky.) If interrupted on a DI, start again. Always get a positive control check for manually connected control surfaces, and do a proper daily inspection.

There are some extraordinary incidents in which clear thinking while under pressure saved the situation. There are also situations when a pilot with a simple decision to take, did not take it. It is hard for most of us to have the detachment of a test pilot, but if you 'self-monitor' your actions, you may be able to snap back into making a decision.

Speaking up

Several airliners have crashed because the co-pilot did not feel able to point out a mistake to the captain. Even if you are P2 and flying with a more experienced pilot, who you consider has chosen an unsafe course of action, always express any doubts that you may have.

Everybody makes mistakes, so if you notice someone about to launch with their air-brakes open, stop the launch and bring it to the attention of the pilot. Anybody can stop a launch and should always do so if they suspect something is wrong, even if the pilot is the CFI.

Note, however, that some gliders have their wheel-brakes at the end of the air-brake control. Applying the wheel-brake stops the glider running over the aerotow-rope. It might, therefore, be helpful to tell your wing-tip runner that you intend to start with the airbrakes open.

Personal attitude

Many varied personalities fly safely, but you should be aware of your emotional tendencies. The US Federal Aviation Administration has identified the following traits as causing problems:

- Macho (tries to impress and takes chances)
- Anti-authority (breaks rules)
- Invulnerable (thinks it will not happen to him/her)
- Impulsive (acts then thinks)
- Resigned (fatalist, so does not act when necessary)

With these characteristics, you can still glide safely, PROVIDED that you are aware of your tendencies and can compensate.

Pilots often knowingly go beyond their privileges and ratings. In studies done elsewhere in the world, 75% of fatal accidents are caused by pilot's attitude while only 25% were down to poor skills. For non-fatal accidents 75% were down to poor skills and 25% were caused by a poor attitude.

PHYSIOLOGY

Eye-sight

Have your eyes tested every two years, and more often if you think that they have changed greatly since the previous check-up. The UK driving requirement is fairly lax, being based on the ability to read a number plate at only 20.5 metres. You should be able to see better than that.

Your medical certificate may require that you carry a spare pair of glasses with you. These must be accessible in flight.

Sunglasses protect a pilot's eyes from glare and from ultra-violet radiation, which is more intense at altitude. UV can cause cancer, cataracts, degeneration of the retina and other unpleasant conditions. Always therefore wear sunglasses when flying in sunny weather.

A good pair of aviation sunglasses, such as *Cloudmaster®*, will also enhance contrast and penetrate haze, improving your ability to see other aircraft, and other interesting features, such as thermal haze-caps, on an otherwise blue day. You can also buy prescription glasses with lenses tinted to your specification.

Optical illusions

Several effects can cause a pilot to misjudge the situation.

- In silhouette it is sometimes difficult to see if a glider is coming or going
- The absence of trees for a pilot who subconsciously uses them to judge height when landing caused the author to be surprised at both Minden and Omarama. (He was P2!)
- A pilot may think the glider is too high when landing on a longer runway than usual and vice versa
- Landing uphill and downhill produces illusions about the approach angle

Barotraumas

Pain and injury caused by differences in pressure are called 'barotrauma'. If you fly high, you may become painfully aware of gas that is trapped in your intestines. Sometimes venting this gas solves the problem, but if this does not work, you might experience severe pain and this may even lower your blood pressure. Shock will be the eventual result, if some relief from distension is not obtained

by descending. You may also be able to reduce the problem in future by avoiding whichever foods or drinks cause gas for you.

Rarely, gas may also be trapped in a decaying tooth and may cause severe pain. Again, the only cure is to descend (and to find a dentist).

Barotraumas in the ears and sinuses are very important to understand, and so is covered extensively in the next section.

Ears

The ear consists of three parts. The outer ear is the part seen on the side of the head, plus the ear canal leading down to the ear drum. The middle ear consists of the ear drum, ear bones, the air spaces behind the ear drum and some cavities. The inner ear contains the organs of balance and hearing with their associated nerve endings.

A pressure difference between the outer ear and the middle ear can cause severe discomfort during flight. This can occur if there is a blockage in the Eustachian tube, which runs from the middle ear to the inner nose. This tube allows the air pressure to equalise on both sides of the eardrum. If the pressure is not equal, the ear feels blocked.

During ascent the air in the middle ear cavity expands, and a small amount of pressure builds up against the ear drum causing the drum to bulge very slightly outwards (which gives a feeling of fullness). As the pressure builds up, the air will automatically escape through the Eustachian tube. Clearing of the ears usually occurs every 500 to 1000 feet of ascent, and so normally there is no problem when going up.

However, the tube is almost closed where it joins back of the nose, so that it is more difficult to let in air to the middle ear than to let it out. Consequently, during descent the Eustachian tube will remain closed, unless actively opened by muscle action or high positive pressure. Yawning, swallowing and chewing provide the muscle action to help the Eustachian tube to open.

If the tube is not opened regularly during descent, a painful pressure difference can develop, especially with a high rate of descent, and if oxygen has been used. The other symptoms include ringing in the ears, temporary deafness, dizziness and nausea.

Human factors

If you are suffering during descent, you should perform the 'Valsalva procedure'. This is done by closing the nose and mouth, putting the tongue against the roof of the mouth and gently blowing against the resistance. This should be done as soon as a feeling of fullness is noted in either ear. Try not to descend at more than 400 feet per minute for long periods. Note that a Valsalva procedure on an ascent will make matters worse.

If there is a very large pressure difference, the ear drum can burst. In this case a doctor should be consulted.

Because the tissues in the nose become swollen when you suffer from a cold, it is more likely that you will have problems equalising the pressure in your middle ear. Your sinuses may also be blocked. The pain of sinus and ear barotraumas from a cold can be cripplingly intense. It can leave the pilots unable to devote sufficient attention to the task of flying. Deciding not to fly is always difficult, but when you have a cold, you are definitely unfit to fly.

If you have a cold, a Valsalva procedure may result in material being carried into the Eustachian tube causing infection of the middle ear. The resulting infection may result in a grounding longer than the original cold.

Spatial disorientation

The inner ear provides hearing through the cochlea, and provides balance and orientation through the semi-circular canals.

Motion sickness is the mismatch between vision and the sensory inputs from the inner ear. There is no infallible cure for this. There are a few experienced glider pilots, and even a WW2 bomber pilot with a DFC and Bar, who have vomited on almost every flight. However, most pilots become accustomed to the sensations within their first few flights.

More subtle disorientation can also occur in cloud, where there are no visual cues. After 10 to 20 seconds of constant turning, no sensation of motion is transmitted to the brain by the inner ear. If the rate of turn is less than two degrees per second, the inner ear will also fail to sense any rotation. The pilot can, therefore, be in a turn and not know it. In addition to not sensing a turn, the inner ear can also make the pilot think that the aircraft is still turning, even after it has straightened up.

The otolith organs are located near the semicircular canals in each ear. They each consist of a tiny jelly-like mass perched on "stilts" of a group of vertical hairs. They sense both head or body tilt and longitudinal acceleration. The otoliths can give erroneous information. In particular they can misinterpret a forwards acceleration as a steep climb, with disastrous consequences if a pilot attempts to correct an illusory steep climb near the ground.

Like the balance organs, the "seat of the pants" pressure centres of the body cannot be relied upon, eg they cannot distinguish between a +3g loop and a +3g steep turn.

In all cases of spatial disorientation, the pilot must rely on the flight instruments when making control inputs, and must be patient until the false sensations dissipate. This requires training, so do not try to teach yourself to fly in cloud. Larger clubs can arrange for training flights in a motor glider. The pupil is equipped with a cap with an excessively large peak that blocks the view outside.

Otherwise stay VMC unless you have had training. Three minutes in cloud is all you will usually have before you lose control.

Dehydration

People should drink more fluid if they are exercising, or if they are sitting for hours under a *Perspex*® canopy. This is especially true when it is hot and at high altitude where the air is much drier.

Dehydration is an insidious condition and may be the cause of more accidents than is generally realised. If you are dehydrated, you will eventually start feeling tired, irritable and confused. You might also get a headache. Strangely, you will not feel thirsty initially. When you feel thirsty, you have been dehydrated for a while. If your urine is deep yellow, you are dehydrated.

The thirst mechanism not only switches on too late, it is turned off too easily. The mechanism also declines after the age of 50. Just a small amount of fluid in the mouth will turn this mechanism off, and so the much needed replacement of water can be delayed. You must, therefore, actively remember to drink often and several mouthfuls at a time while flying and before you take off. A hydrator, such as a *Camelbak*®, will allow you to drink frequently with the minimum of distraction. (If buying a *Camelbak*®, buy the 3-litre size.)

Dehydration is hastened by drinking coffee and tea before a flight, because these contain a diuretic. Excess alcohol the night before or diarrhoea will also mean that you start the day by being dehydrated.

If you get seriously dehydrated, do not fly again until you have drunk enough water to make your urine almost clear. This may take more than 24 hours.

It is sufficient to drink pure water. Despite advertisements for 'sports-drinks', salts are quickly replaced by a normal balanced diet, except for cases of extreme exercise and extreme heat.

Direct sunlight on your head will exacerbate dehydration, and can significantly reduce your ability to concentrate. NEVER take off without a narrow-brimmed hat in hot or sunny conditions. (A large-brimmed hat or a peaked cap will severely interfere with your look-out.)

Oxygen
The proportion of oxygen in the air remains constant with increasing altitude. However the lower pressure means that there is less oxygen to diffuse through your lungs into your blood.

Atmospheric pressure falls with height so that:
- At sea level   = 1013hPa
- 10,000 feet   = 700hPa
- 18,000 feet   = 500hPa

The respiratory process is governed by chemical receptors that are in the brain and that are also situated alongside certain arteries. These receptors monitor the levels of oxygen and carbon dioxide. The receptors are more sensitive to changes in carbon dioxide than oxygen, and so it is the level of CO_2 that mainly regulates your breathing. Since you are doing no additional work at altitude, the level of CO_2 in your blood remains as it is on the ground. Consequently you will continue to breathe normally even though you are receiving insufficient oxygen, until very low levels of oxygen are reached.

Lack of oxygen is called 'hypoxia'. It is another insidious process which produces symptoms similar to drinking alcohol. The features of hypoxia are:
- Personality change
- Lack of insight
- Loss of judgement
- Loss of self-criticism
- Over-confidence
- Euphoria
- Loss of memory
- Mental and muscular incoordination
- Sensory loss, including worsening eyesight
- Cyanosis
- Semi-consciousness, unconsciousness and eventually death

Cyanosis is the bluish colouration of the skin, nail-beds and mucous membranes. In the presence of significant anaemia, it will not appear. Normal subjects breathing air are noticeably cyanotic above 17,000 feet to 19,000 feet, but you may have already passed out by the time that this symptom appears.

A rapid ascent without oxygen will allow a higher altitude to be reached before the symptoms of hypoxia develop. It is even possible that the first serious symptom to occur in these circumstances may be unconsciousness.

In short, you cannot easily tell when you need oxygen, except by looking at the altimeter. Even if you are only suffering from mild hypoxia, you will feel a sense of exhilaration or security and may be quite proud of your proficiency, even though you are on the verge of complete incompetence.

Just breathing harder will not counteract the lack of oxygen, and is positively dangerous because this will adversely disturb your carbon dioxide levels (see hyperventilation).

The Air Navigation Order makes it mandatory for private flights to carry such a serviceable system if flying above FL130, or if flying between FL100 and FL130 for more than 30 minutes, and for the crew to use it.

Though tolerance of low pressure partly depends on the individual, it is only possible for anyone to acclimatise fully by living at altitude for weeks. Stress, high g, some drugs such as alcohol and anti-histamines, low temperatures, many types of illness, fatigue or physical activity reduce tolerance, so that the symptoms of hypoxia can occur at a lower altitude. Hypoxia will also occur at lower altitudes for smokers.

If your oxygen system fails at 20,000 feet, with minimal activity and complete relaxation, people have typically between 5 and 10 minutes of consciousness. By 25,000 feet this time has fallen to 2-3 minutes. You must therefore know how your oxygen system works, and monitor the remaining reserves.

Up to 33,700 feet, receiving 100% oxygen has the same result as breathing air at ground level. At 39,000 feet, receiving 100% oxygen is equivalent to being at 10,000 feet, but in practice oxygen systems are never completely efficient. 35,000 feet is the safe limit with even the best diluter-demand systems with a mask.

Hyperventilation

It is possible to breathe too hard and too rapidly resulting in another condition called 'hyperventilation'. It usually arises because of anxiety. It is caused by the over-reduction of carbon dioxide in the blood.

The early symptoms of hyperventilation are: light-headedness, dizziness, anxiety and a superficial tingling in the hands, feet and around the lips. Later muscle spasms of the limbs and face may occur.

The cure is not to panic even more and to consciously reduce the rate of breathing. Though scary, hyperventilation is not usually dangerous on the ground, but in the air it would be a major distraction.

The symptoms of hypoxia and hyperventilation are similar. Since hypoxia is much more common at altitude and is more serious, if in doubt, use oxygen. If you are sure that the problem is hyperventilation, breathing and re-breathing from a bag helps. If there is no bag to hand, you could try re-breathing from cupped hands.

Scuba diving

A diver must breathe air under pressure, which forces air into the blood. It takes time for the nitrogen to escape after surfacing. After scuba diving, the guidelines are "do not fly within 12 hours of swimming using compressed air and avoid flying for 24 hours if a depth of 30 feet has been exceeded". You run the risk of the decompression sickness if you fly too soon after diving, because the trapped nitrogen may form bubbles in the joints and other organs. Divers gave names to the symptoms depending on where they occurred ('bends', 'creeps', 'chokes' and 'staggers'). The risks increase with age, obesity and re-exposure.

Hypothermia

The lower temperature at height can create a condition called 'hypothermia'. An unexpectedly long flight in cold weather can quickly produce the following symptoms:

- Drowsiness
- Weakness and loss of coordination
- Slurred speech
- Confusion
- Uncontrollable shivering
- Aggressive or withdrawn behaviour

Violent shuddering is a clear sign to land immediately. It is unlikely you would lose consciousness in a glider, but your concentration may be seriously impaired before this stage is reached.

Much heat is lost through the head, so wear a woolly hat on cold days.

G effects

Few gliders can safely pull very high g, but be aware that a lack of oxygen reaching the brain in high g manoeuvres can cause a black-out even at low altitudes. Grey-outs (loss of colour vision) start as low as 3g for untrained pilots at sea level.

Everyone has their own tolerance level to g-forces but factors which may affect your tolerance include tiredness, hypoxia, fitness, dehydration and the 'after effects' of alcohol. However, regular aerobatics and tensing of your muscles can improve your tolerance.

Negative g is usually regarded as being much more unpleasant than the equivalent amount of positive g. Gliders are also less able to withstand negative g. Be aware that small number of people are unduly sensitive to low or negative g. Some of these people move their heads back and push the stick forward. Since the glider may be already pointing at the ground, this can be alarming for the other pilot. However people with this sensitivity rarely reach solo.

Carbon monoxide

In a motor glider, a faulty exhaust system could leak carbon monoxide into the cockpit. It is difficult to recognise because it is odourless and colourless. The symptoms are

- Headache
- Fatigue

- Shortness of breath
- Impaired judgement and confusion
- Dizziness and fainting

It is particularly dangerous if it happens when hypoxia is also beginning to occur.

Carbon monoxide poisoning can be detected in powered aircraft (and homes where it kills thirty people a year in the UK) by fitting an inexpensive detector.

Summary

A pilot's physical and mental state is the most important factor in flying safely. Almost all the sections in this chapter contain advice that will maintain your alertness while flying. In particular:

- Keep a good look-out
- Maintain familiarity/currency
- Be aware of your mental attitude
- Do not get dehydrated
- Know the height at which you must use oxygen
- Minimise stress/workload
- Do not descend too fast without equalising the pressure in your ears
- Never fly with a cold
- Be aware of the effect of alcohol, even the night before a flight

Questions

1. At what height does the law require the use of oxygen?
2. What is the approximate time of useful consciousness at 20,000 feet for an average person without supplementary oxygen assuming minimal activity?
3. You are at 5,000 feet and after a scare you feel dizzy, what could be the problem?
4. You are suffering from a heavy cold which has caused a blocked nose and/or blocked sinuses. Is it safe to fly after taking a decongestant?
5. As you are descending from a diamond height gain, you experience severe pain in your ears. What should you do?
6. During a long cross-country flight, you are feeling drowsy and irritable, what might you do improve the situation?
7. You have been stowing equipment in your glider, and so appear to be slow to get into it. The launch-point controller unjustifiably questions your IQ. What might be the effect on your concentration?
8. You are 53, but not an instructor, when is your next medical certificate due?

PRINCIPLES OF FLIGHT

Introduction

Of all subjects in gliding, the principles of flight and their implications are the largest. They have been extensively covered in many books. The basic principles have therefore only been summarised in this chapter, which should be treated as revision notes rather than a complete account.

How a wing works

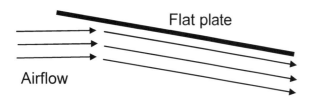

Even a flat plate set at a shallow angle to an air-flow will provide a substantial amount of lift by deflecting air downwards. Slightly increasing the angle of this plate to the air-flow will increase the amount of lift generated. However, the flow of the air over the upper surface of a flat plate is chaotic, and so it would be an inefficient wing.

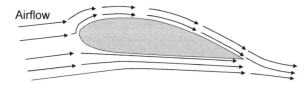

A well designed wing directs the air downwards better than a flat plate, especially over its upper surface. The curve on the top surface makes a dramatic difference. It allows the air to flow smoothly over the wing and to accelerate. When air accelerates, its pressure falls. Lower pressure is also created above the wing because some of the air that would have been there has been deflected below the wing. The difference in pressure between the top and bottom surfaces of the wing provides the upward force.

The pressure decrease above the upper surface of a glider's wing is much greater than the pressure increase below the lower surface, and so the upper surface generates the great majority of the lift.

If the air-speed is increased, the amount of lift also increases for a given angle of the wing to the air-flow.

It is difficult to expand on this explanation without resorting to mathematics, but it is possible to be a safe and successful glider pilot without studying this further.

Angle of attack and relative air-flow

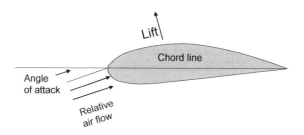

The movement of the glider through the air causes the air to flow past the glider in exactly the opposite direction. This air-flow is known as the 'relative air-flow'. Since the glider is usually descending through the air, the relative air-flow usually comes from slightly below.

The angle at which the air-flow arrives is called the 'angle of attack'. The term 'chord of the wing' means a straight line from the leading edge to the trailing edge. The chord line is always straight. This is often used as the datum when measuring the angle of attack.

An increase in the angle of attack initially increases the amount of lift produced by a glider's wings but then the air-speed decays because of drag.

The direction of the lift force produced by the wing is at right angles to the <u>relative air flow</u>, not to the chord line. This means that the lift force acts slightly forwards in level flight.

The angle that the wings are set in the fuselage relative to the centre line of the fuselage is another different angle, known as the 'angle of incidence'.

Control surfaces

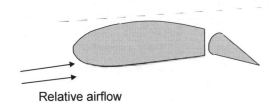

Relative airflow

Ailerons, flaps, elevators and rudders are all control surfaces. These are used to alter the curve (the 'camber') of the wing's surface, of the tail-plane or of the fin to which they are attached. Changing the curvature affects the lift that is generated by effectively increasing the angle of attack.

In the diagram above, the curvature of the wing has been increased by the control surface moving down and so it would generate more lift.

Wing shapes

The curve of the wing is known as the 'profile' and these days it is the subject of much computer analysis to achieve as smooth a flow as possible. Any turbulence means drag and so a loss of efficiency.

On some gliders, the angle of attack at the wing-tip is reduced compared with the angle of attack at the root. In effect the wing-tips are slightly twisted. The smaller angle of attack at the tip means that it is less likely to stall there before the root. If there were a stall at the tip first, it would create drag at the tip and this force at the end of the wing would initiate a spin as soon as the glider stalled. This twist to prevent tip-stalling is known as 'wash-out'.

Forces

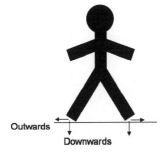

Outwards

Downwards

If maths passed you by at school, you need to learn two very simple concepts about forces. Firstly it is sometimes easier to think about a force as consisting of two parts (known as 'components').

For example, if you stand with your legs apart, the floor experiences a force from each foot as a vertical component downwards and an outwards component. (The outward force can be demonstrated by standing in socks on a highly polished floor, but caution should be exercised!)

You can also think of forces being combined into a single force, known as a 'resultant'.

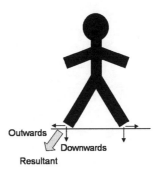

Outwards

Downwards

Resultant

In this example, the combination of the outwards component and the downwards component can be thought of as a single resultant force acting in an intermediate direction.

A force applied to an unconstrained object results in a change in its velocity. For example, push steadily on a supermarket trolley and the velocity will increase. The greater the force, the greater is the acceleration. If you make the trolley twice as heavy with shopping, you will have to push twice as hard to achieve the same acceleration to the shortest queue. Once the force ceases or is balanced by something else, the acceleration ceases and the object then continues at a new constant velocity. Of course the average trolley experiences friction from its wheels and air resistance called drag. This provides a decelerating force in the opposite direction to the trolley's motion and so some pushing is still needed to maintain a constant speed (and direction!)

Forces on the glider in flight

There are only three forces on a glider in free flight: lift, weight and drag. At a steady speed they balance each other. If they do not balance, the forces will accelerate the glider until they balance, (or until the ground is reached).

We have already described the source of the first of the forces, the lift force. Although lift is produced across the wing, the force can be thought as emanating about one third of the way back from the leading edge.

Principles of flight

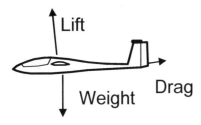

The weight of an object is the second of the three forces. It can be assumed to act through a single point, known as the 'centre of gravity'. If the glider were placed on a pivot at its centre of gravity, it would balance. The weight of the glider (or anything else) always acts vertically down.

Drag is the third force and is usually the smallest of the forces. The various forms of drag all act in parallel to the relative air-flow, ie at right angles to the lift. (There is more about drag later.)

Since the lift from the wings acts perpendicularly to the relative air-flow, it does not usually act vertically upwards, but slightly forwards of vertical. When the nose of the glider is lowered, the direction of the lift force is tilted even further forward and this accelerates the glider forwards. The weight always acts vertically downwards, so that it cannot provide any forward force. In an unpowered glider there is no thrust.

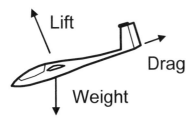

If the nose is lowered, the vertical component of the lift is reduced because more of the lift is acting forwards. With less lift the rate of descent increases, ie the glider dives. The rate of vertical descent and horizontal speed will continue to increase until the drag has increased sufficiently to counter-balance the forces of lift and weight. Once the forces are back in balance, the glider will continue at a higher but steady speed.

The lift and drag forces together can be thought of as a single resultant force that is known as the 'total reaction'. This combined force acts upwards from a point somewhere in the middle of the fuselage

called the 'centre of pressure'. In steady flight it is at the same place as the centre of gravity.

Forces in a turn

In a turn, the same three forces still affect a glider. Banking the wings means that the lift from the wings is no longer acting just forwards and vertically. A component of the lift force is also directed sideways and it is this component of the lift force that makes the glider change direction.

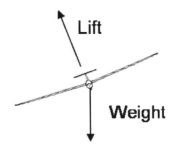

Because the lift is no longer acting vertically, more lift is needed to compensate. By moving the stick back, the angle of attack of the wing is increased and this creates more lift. The forces in the turn therefore come into balance. Moving the stick back also tightens the turn, because of the greater sideways component from the extra lift.

More lift force from the wings is needed to force the glider round an even steeper turn. Increasing the angle of attack to achieve this extra lift requires increasingly greater aft movement of the stick. Because it is more difficult to increase the angle of attack in a steep turn, it is more difficult to stall, so turns near the ground are safer if they are well banked.

Types of drag

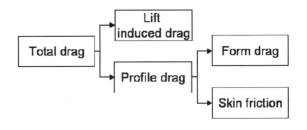

Drag is the force that resists the glider's movement through the air. There are two basic causes: 'lift-induced drag' and 'profile drag'.

Lift-induced drag

The angle of attack creates high pressure below the wing and lower pressure above. Behind the wing, the high and low pressure air-flows from above and below the wing re-combine and produce drag, much of it from a vortex at the wing-tip The drag is greatest at low speed when the wing has a high angle of attack, ie when the pressure difference is greatest. From this maximum at stalling speed, lift-induced drag then <u>decreases</u> with the square of the speed.

The 'aspect ratio' is wing-span divided by the mean width of the chord, ie the average of the distance from the leading edge to the trailing edge. High aspect wings have less lift-induced drag because efficient lift is produced by all along the large wing-span and only a small part of the total length of the wing at the tips is producing drag. Gliders have high aspect ratios, ie gliders have long narrow wings, but you probably knew this already.

Winglets are a way of reducing lift-induced drag by managing the way in which the high pressure air meets the low pressure air at the wing-tips.

Profile drag

Profile drag has two causes: skin friction and form drag. Skin friction is caused by the air rubbing against the surface of the glider. Consequently a well polished, clean glider will have lower skin friction than a neglected glider.

Form drag has several causes. Fundamentally it is caused by the shape of the glider and the resulting frontal area that it presents to the air-flow. Additional form drag can be added by non-essential impediments such as an un-retracted undercarriage. This is called 'parasitic drag'.

Leakage of air from a high pressure area also causes a type of form drag called 'leakage drag'. This can occur if the wing roots have not been taped, or if air can flow past the hinges in the control surfaces. Leakage drag can also be created by air entering the fuselage round the edge of the canopy or via the wheel-well.

Another sort of form drag is 'interference drag'. This occurs if there is sharp angle between the components of the glider such as the wing and the fuselage. The sharp angle prevents smooth air-flow.

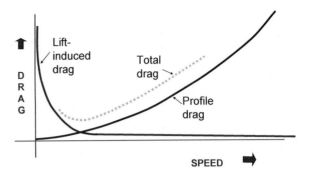

Between stall and V_{NE}, the different types of profile drag all <u>increase</u> with the square of the speed. This is in contrast with the lift-induced drag that decreases with the square of the speed.

Consequently there is a speed at which the total drag is at a minimum. At this speed the glider has its best glide angle (see the diagram above).

Ground effect

When a glider flies less than half a wing-span above the ground, the air below the wing is deflected downwards as usual, but it is then reflected upwards by the ground, so that the air under the wing is slightly compressed. This increased pressure below the wing generates more lift. The wing-tip vortices are also impeded by the ground, so that the lift-induced drag is reduced. The glider therefore floats above the ground for longer than might have been expected, especially if the airbrakes are not used.

Ailerons

When a glider banks, the lift that each wing generates is affected because both ailerons change the camber of parts of the wings. However, changing the amount of lift generated by each wing also affects the amount of drag that is produced. The 'up-going' wing will produce more profile drag and lift-induced drag while and the 'down-going' wing will produce relatively less.

The large span of gliders means that much of the aileron drag is produced at a distance from the fuselage, creating considerable leverage. The glider is therefore yawed in the 'wrong' direction, and this is known as 'adverse yaw'. Applying 'into-turn' rudder at the same time as aileron provides another opposing yawing force, allowing the glider to turn more smoothly.

Differential ailerons are one method of reducing adverse yaw. Differential ailerons deflect the down aileron much less than the up aileron, so that the additional profile drag from the down aileron is much less than that from the up aileron.

Once established in the turn, the outer wing will be travelling further and therefore faster than the inner wing. The outer wing will therefore generate more lift than the inner wing so that the glider will have a tendency to increase the bank still further. Some opposite aileron is therefore often needed in the turn to counteract this tendency for the bank to increase. The additional lift from the outer wing may also generate enough additional drag on some gliders to require a small amount of 'into-turn' rudder. In other words you may be in a well co-ordinated turn in some gliders with slightly crossed controls.

Ailerons (and the other control surfaces) are carefully balanced to ensure that they cannot wobble at a resonant frequency, with the rather innocent-sounding name of 'flutter'. However flutter in aircraft can be much more violent that the beat of a butterfly's wing. In a well maintained glider, you are unlikely to experience the flutter associated with high air-speeds. If it occurs it could be an alarming vibration. You should slow down to avoid damaging the control surfaces and then land immediately to allow for investigation before the glider flies again.

The three axes

When a glider is flying at a steady speed, the three forces are in equilibrium and there is no acceleration in any of the three axes. However the pilot or the air can disturb this peaceful state. Fortunately gliders are designed to counteract these changes.

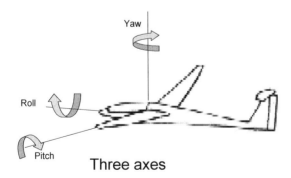

Three axes

The three axes: pitch, roll and yaw, are fixed relative to the aircraft, irrespective of which direction it is pointing.

Stability in roll

Dihedral is the name given to the way that wings are angled slightly upwards, as can be seen below by a frontal view of an ASW28.

Each wing of this glider is therefore slightly banked, so that the lift from each wing is not acting quite vertically upwards. If the aircraft banks slightly, the lift from lower wing will now act straight upwards.

Less lift   More lift

The vertical component of the lift from the lower wing is now greater than the vertical component of lift from the higher wing. This imbalance of forces will try to level the wings.

Dihedral, therefore, resists banking movement automatically, providing 'lateral stability'. However, too much stability would make a glider unpleasant to fly and it would lose performance, so the designers therefore have to make a compromise between roll rate and stability.

Stability in pitch

Wings are naturally unstable and will always try to pitch downwards. The tail-plane is therefore used to provide a down-force that tries to raise the nose.

When a glider's nose pitches up, the angle of attack of the tail-plane increases, and this decreases the down-force. Conversely, when the nose is lowered, the tail-plane will produce a greater down-force. Consequently the tail-plane resists pitching movement, and is said to provide 'longitudinal stability'.

The force generated by the tail-plane can be modified by changing its camber by using the elevator. This moves the glider's nose up or down, increasing or decreasing the angle of attack of the wings. A long fuselage gives leverage to the tail-plane and rudder, both of which would otherwise have to be bigger to achieve the same effect.

Fin, rudder and stability in yaw

The fin provides stability in the third axis by keeping the fuselage pointing in the direction of flight. If the glider yaws right, the increased air-flow onto the left side of the fin will tend to straighten the glider up.

The rudder works in much the same way as the horizontal control surfaces by changing the camber of the fin, generating 'horizontal lift' to the left or to the right to yaw the glider.

Flaps

An unflapped wing is most efficient at only one speed, but since gliders fly at a range of speeds, flaps are used on some gliders. Flaps change the camber along much of the length of both wings. The pilot can therefore select the camber that is appropriate to the speed at which the glider is flying. When the flaps are pointing down it is known as 'positive flap' and when pointing upwards, 'negative flap'. When zero flap is set, the wing behaves like that of an unflapped glider.

When a glider's flaps are moved down & up, they have the effect of moving the centre of lift forward & back. In other words a flapped glider, when flying fast with negative flaps (ie raised flaps), will be less nose-down than the equivalent unflapped glider at the same speed.

Lowering the flaps increases lift and so increases drag and stress. Consequently there is usually a maximum speed in the flight manual at which positive flaps can be deployed. For this reason you should slow up before using positive flaps. However to get the benefits of the correct flap setting, and to reduce stress on the flaps, you should change to negative flap as soon as you start speeding up for the inter-thermal glide.

When full positive flap is selected, the ailerons are also pointed downwards by the mechanism. If a further downwards move of the ailerons is made, only a little extra lift is produced, especially at low speeds. Consequently at low speed, such as when taking off on aerotow or on the landing roll, the amount of aileron control is sometimes insufficient. For this reason, flight manuals usually suggest starting the take-off and finishing the landing roll in negative flap.

If the flaps also move at the same time as the ailerons, they are known as 'flaperons'. They improve the roll rate.

Airbrakes and limiting of speed

The use of airbrakes to increase the rate of descent for landing should already be well understood. They increase drag, reduce lift and increase stability. However, airbrakes can also be used to limit speed if control is lost when flying in cloud, or if undertaking aerobatic manoeuvres. The airbrakes will help to keep the speed of a modern glider below V_{NE}, but only if it is not diving too steeply (typically by not more than 45°).

Do not open the airbrakes whilst in a spin, or else you may delay recovery. It is only in the dive after the spin that the speed builds up.

If you deploy the airbrakes to stop over-speeding, it is important to open them early. Otherwise, to slow up, you are likely to have to pull some g. Opening the air-brakes increases the stress on the wing. This is because the airbrakes reduce the lift from the centre section of the wing, while the tips are still being bent up by the lift that the outer part of the wings are generating. However, it is generally better to open the airbrakes and limit the speed than to keep them closed and have the additional strength margin. Consult the flight manual of your glider. At high speed the airbrakes will also slam fully open with considerable force.

If you deploy the airbrakes to limit your speed, remember to close them after regaining control, otherwise you may stall the glider as the nose is raised.

As you try out different types of gliders, you may encounter different types of devices for approach control, such as trailing edge airbrakes, spoilers and tail-chutes. It is important that you understand the characteristics of these types of airbrakes before flying with them. Read the flight manuals.

Flow over the wing

Even though air is flowing over the wing, the layer of air molecules next to the wing surface will stick to it and so will not move. The next layer of molecules will try to stick to the first layer but may be dragged along slightly by the next layer above and so on. This increase in air-speed continues outwards from the wing until a place is reached where the air is unaffected by the wing. This region from the surface of the wing to where you reach the undisturbed air is known as the 'boundary layer'. Drag is minimised when the amount of air involved in this boundary layer is minimised. More air in the boundary layer increases the amount of energy that is lost through drag.

The boundary layer may be smoothly flowing or it may be turbulent. When the air-flow is smooth, it is known as 'laminar flow'. In laminar flow there is a steady increase in the speed of the air-flow from the wing's surface outwards and the layer is thin. A thin, smoothly flowing layer involves the minimum amount of air and so it produces the least drag. However a turbulent boundary layer creates more drag because of the sudden changes in its air-speed and the greater quantity of air that is involved.

The further along that a laminar layer persists next to the wing's surface, the better. Glass-fibre has allowed the designers of modern gliders to produce wings with smooth surfaces that allow laminar flow to continue from the leading edge over much of the surface. However the wings of wooden gliders are not so precisely shaped, so that the laminar flow does not persist for as long.

The point at which the air changes from laminar flow to turbulence is known as the 'transition point'. Beyond the transition point for a modern wing, the air may continue to flow in a relatively thin boundary layer, even though it is turbulent, producing only a little extra drag.

In some wing-shapes all the laminar air in the boundary layer suddenly breaks away en masse from the surface before the layer becomes turbulent. Beneath this layer of organised air, a large region of turbulence appears, creating more drag. Designers therefore sometimes deliberately trip the air-flow into a turbulent state because a thin turbulent layer of air will not break away from the wing's surface en masse. Some gliders therefore have 'turbulator' tape on the underside of the wings, on the elevator and on the fin to achieve this.

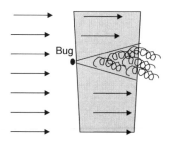

View from above wing

At the leading edge of a wing the boundary layer is only 0.5mm thick, increasing to about 5mm further

back. Consequently, even small irregularities can affect this thin layer. Smooth surfaces are essential to get a good performance from a modern glider's wing.

Objects such as insects and raindrops on the leading edge, prevent laminar flow, not just directly downwind, but also in a wide turbulent wake either side of the obstruction. Bear this in mind when calculating your final glide, if the leading edges of the wings are covered in insects.

The extreme case is when the wings are covered in frost, snow or raindrops before launch. In these circumstances do not launch until the wings and tail-plane have been cleared. The lift with this contamination is severely reduced.

Stalls

You should already be well acquainted with stalls and recovery from them, so this section only explains their causes.

A stall occurs when the angle of attack increases to typically 15°. At this angle the boundary layer above the wing soon becomes chaotic and separates from the wing. The partial vacuum formed in this region is filled with air flowing from elsewhere and this causes great turbulence on the upper surface.

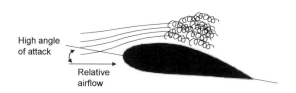

This turbulence causes the characteristic buffeting and produces much more drag. The lift produced by the wing reaches a maximum just before the stall and then reduces rapidly at higher angles and slower speeds.

In normal flight, a high angle of attack is only achievable at low speed. At higher speeds the glider merely climbs when the stick is moved backwards. At low speed the glider has insufficient energy to climb and so a high angle of attack is then possible.

The turbulence in the boundary layer needed to create a stall can be caused by bugs, rain-drops, frost and snow on the wings. These will cause the stall to occur at a higher speed. (See also *High speed stalls* later.) Do not take off without clearing the wings if the wing surface has any water or detritus.

In well designed wing, a straight stall occurs first the wing roots and the stall then spreads outwards to the tips. Stalling first at the tip would make spins more likely. At the stall the centre of pressure also moves backwards and behind the centre of gravity. The weight of the glider will therefore cause the nose to pitch down, which is characteristic of gliders at the stall (provided they are being flown within the ballast limits).

Spins

Spins can arise from a slow over-ruddered turn, from a turn at low speed after a failed winch-launch, or even while thermalling with excessive rudder. You should already know how to prevent these spins, and how to recover.

Stalls and spins are both caused by high angles of attack, but in the case of spins, the additional factor is that one wing stalls first, often because of yaw. Unlike a straight stall, the tip of the wing stalls first in a spin. The additional drag from the tip of the stalled wing causes the glider to rotate about the stalled wing. This is known as 'autorotation'.

In the case of a failed winch-launch, the glider may quickly achieve a horizontal attitude, but it still has a very low air-speed. Its wings are generating little lift, and so the glider begins to move vertically downwards with the nose high. Its relative air-flow therefore mainly comes from below and impinges on the wing at a high angle of attack. The glider is therefore deeply stalled. If you then add in some rudder and aileron before the glider has recovered from this stall, one wing is very likely to drop and a full spin will develop. Attaining approach speed before turning after a winch-launch failure is therefore essential.

Rotating objects such as spinning gliders have odd properties, as the slow precession of a spinning top demonstrates. The physics is complex, but when you stop the glider spinning, the nose pitches down.

The position of the centre of gravity has a big effect on the ease of recovery from a spin. If the pilot is too light, it is more difficult to reduce the angle of attack and un-stall the glider. It is also possible to create the same effect as a light pilot by taking off with your tail-dolly attached.
It is usually recommended that you become familiar with the spinning characteristics of your glider, but

there are a few provisos, including reading the glider's flight manual. Many open-class gliders are a real handful when spinning, and it is best not to practise spins with these types. Spinning gliders that are full of water ballast is also not recommended, because of the higher stall speed, greater inertia and higher loads when pulling out of a dive.

When flapped gliders are flown in positive flap settings (eg for thermalling or landing) the handling often deteriorates, making the glider more likely to spin. However the maximum speed for positive flaps is easily exceeded in the recovery dive. It is therefore usually recommended that you do not practise spinning flapped gliders in the configuration in which they are most likely to spin!

Stalling at higher speeds

A stall will occur when the critical angle of attack is reached, whatever the air-speed. At higher speeds in level flight it is usually impossible to achieve a high angle of attack, unless you move the stick sharply back. The glider merely climbs instead.

High angle attack when pulling out of a dive

High angle of attack

Direction of motion

However, in some situations the wings may already have an increased angle of attack because they are already being required to generate more lift. This situation can arise when the glider is heavier, when the glider is turning, or when pulling g at the bottom of a dive. A high angle of attack can also occur when the glider is being winch-launched. Suddenly rotating into the full climb will produce a high angle of attack, as will the high downward forces at the top of the winch-launch. Any of these conditions are said to create a 'high wing-loading'. The high wing-loading has made it possible to reach the high angle of attack, so that it is possible to stall at a higher speed.

The stall speed increases as the square root of the wing loading. This means that if the glider experiences 2g in a tight turn, the stall speed is 1.414 times higher than in normal flight.

High speed stalls are not just a novelty. Like normal stalls, high speed stalls can develop into spins, given enough yaw. The departure is rapid and is a "flick" manoeuvre that can overstress the glider.

Stalling during wire-launching

In a wire launch, the nose of the glider can be pointing skywards, but the actual direction of motion is not as steep, so that the relative air-flow arrives at a high angle of attack. Stalls can therefore occur at much higher speeds than normal. The stall

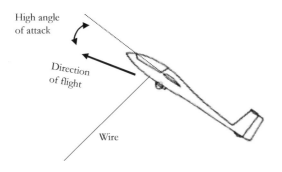

speed at maximum climb-rate on a wire-launch can be about 40% higher than normal. A minimum safety speed should therefore be observed on wire-launches of 50% above the normal stalling speed.

Glider performance

Two of the key measures of a glider's performance are its minimum sink rate and its best glide angle. Knowing the difference between these speeds is important for cross-country flying. Flying at the minimum sink speed enables you to stay airborne for as long as possible, but you will not travel as far as if you fly at the speed for the best glide.

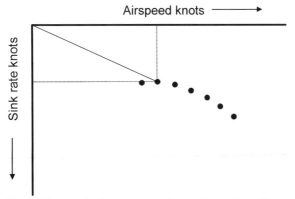

The glide angle is expressed as the ratio of the distance travelled to height lost in the same time. The ratio of the horizontal speed versus the vertical

speed gives the same answer. (If you glide at 40 knots for an hour and experience a 2 knot sink rate, you will travel 40 nautical miles and descend 2 nautical miles. The glide ratio is 20 using both methods).

By measuring the rate of sink at various air-speeds you can derive a set of data and plot this on a graph. (Doing this in reality is a complex task.) The points can be connected by a line known as the 'polar curve'. Each type of glider has a unique polar curve.

The 'origin' for a polar curve is where the air-speed is zero and the sink rate is zero. In the above diagram a line has been drawn from the origin to the point with minimum sink. The slope of the line from the origin is the glide angle, because it is the ratio of the distance along the air-speed axis to the distance along the sink rate axis.

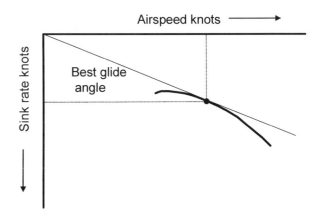

You can draw a whole series of lines from the origin to each of the data points. Each line will show the glide angle for that speed. However the glide angle, in which we are most interested, is the best glide angle, ie the line with the least slope. In the diagram above, the line has been drawn from the origin to the point representing the best glide angle. Again you can read off the air-speed and sink rate for this point, and so calculate the glide ratio. This glide angle is shallower than the glide angle at the minimum rate of sink.

All the other lines from the origin to the various data points will be steeper than the line of the best glide angle. Consequently, the line for the best glide angle will only just graze the polar curve, ie it is a tangent.

The adjusted polar curve

The polar curve has wider uses. Firstly, consider the effect on the polar curve if the glider is in sinking air. In addition to its own natural rate of sink (say 1.3 knots), the additional sink might be 2 knots, making a total rate of sink of 3.3 knots.

You could plot an entirely new polar curve for these sinking conditions and draw lines from the origin as before. However, there is a wide range of possible values for sink and lift, and this would mean drawing multiple graphs. Consequently, instead of drawing a new graph, the origin for drawing the glide angle line is moved.

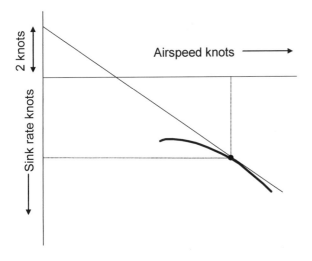

For air sinking at 2 knots, you merely draw a tangent from a new origin that is 2 knots further up the axis. As the diagram above shows, the best glide angle in sinking air is at a higher speed.

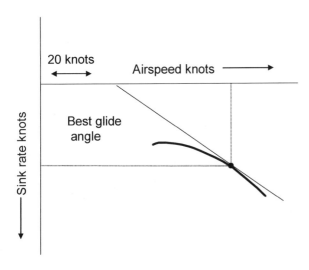

The polar curve can also be used to estimate the effect of the wind. If you fly into a 20 knot headwind, the ground speed is reduced by 20 knots.

The zero point is now effectively at 20 knots of air-speed, moving the start of the line for the best glide angle to the right (see diagram above). The best glide angle for a headwind is, therefore, also at a higher speed.

Estimating your cross country speed

Polar curves are the basis for much of the theory about achieving the best cross-country speed. In particular, the best speeds to fly, given the strength of the thermals, are associated with Paul MacCready. Some gliders have a 'rotatable' MacCready ring around the air-speed indicator that has been calibrated using the polar curve. Electronic flight directors also use these principles.

While it is not essential to know this, there is yet another useful trick with the polar curve, namely for a given thermal strength you can estimate your theoretical cross country speed.

You can assume that:
- The height gained on a cross country flight equals the height lost (apart from a minus sign), if you ignore your start height
- The total time of the flight is the sum of the time spent climbing and time spent between climbs
- Speed between climbs is the task distance divided by the time spent between climbs
- The height lost is the sink rate between thermals multiplied by the time spent between climbs
- The height gained is the average climb rate multiplied by the total time spent climbing
- Average cross country speed (XC speed) is the task distance divided by the total flight time (excluding time before the start)

If you put these statements into algebraic form, you can derive the following expression:

$$\frac{\text{Average XC speed}}{\text{Average climb rate}} = \frac{\text{Speed between climbs}}{\text{Average climb rate} - \text{sink rate}}$$

This expression can be seen in the diagram below as the ratios of two proportional triangles. (Remember that the sink rate is negative so it adds to the average climb rate in the expression).

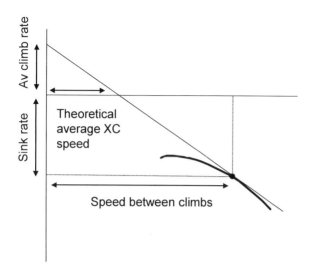

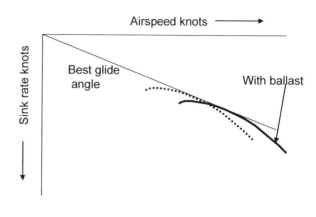

Consequently, if you draw a line from the best glide speed on the polar curve to the point on the vertical axis for the expected average climb rate, you can read off your best speed between climbs and your cross country speed for a given climb rate.

However you can improve the glide angle by pulling up when passing through rising air and by avoiding sink by following the "lines of energy" ie the paths that will take you through the most lift and the least sink. Your cross country speed can therefore often exceed the theoretical maximum.

The most important factors in increasing your cross-country speed are therefore:

- Maximising your average climb rate by stopping to circle in only the strongest lift
- Minimising your average sink rate by flying in rising air even when flying straight and by avoiding sinking air
- Adjusting your tactics as the conditions change

Flying at exactly the right speed between climbs is less important than these three factors.

Water ballast

Another use of the polar curve is when determining the speed to fly when the glider is carrying ballast.

The polar curve is shifted downwards in the diagram below, as might be expected with the additional weight, but it is also shifted to the right. A ballasted glider will therefore have the same best glide angle as an un-ballasted glider, but at a higher speed.

If you plan to use water ballast, you should read the relevant section of the flight manual for the glider. Adding water ballast to the wings may increase the weight ahead of the glider's centre of gravity. To avoid flying a glider that is too nose-heavy, some gliders has a fin-tank as well that will counter-balance the water in the wings and allow the glider to glide in an attitude that is less nose-down and without excessive back trim, so minimising drag.

However, there are penalties to pay for carrying ballast. In particular, a ballasted glider climbs more slowly because of its greater weight. The break-even point for a standard-class glider in still air, when it becomes worth keeping ballast, is when the actual achieved rates of climb exceed about three knots. A three-knot average means the climb rate achieved from the time you stop travelling on track to the time that you set off again. This average is not the same as a momentary rate of climb when you have found the core of a thermal. Three-knot achieved rates of climb are relatively uncommon in the UK.

The tactics of using ballast are beyond the scope of this book, but it is sufficient to say that it is unnecessary for early cross-country pilots even to consider using it.

Why gliders speed up in lift

You may have noticed that air-speed increases when you fly into the core of a thermal. The reason was first described by Dr AH Yates. An up-draught will increase the angle of attack because the airflow comes more from below. Since the lift from the wings always acts at right angles to the relative airflow, the lift acts further forward and accelerates the glider.

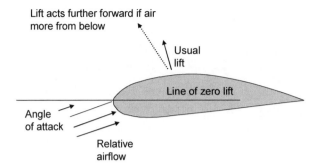

Questions

1. Name the forces on a glider when it is flying straight at a steady speed.
2. Name the forces on a glider when it is in a well banked turn at a steady speed.
3. Why does a glider increase its speed in a turn unless you move the stick back?
4. How does profile drag change with air-speed between the stall and V_{NE}?
5. How does lift-induced drag change with air-speed between the stall and V_{NE}?
6. At what speed is total drag at a minimum?
7. Why put sealing tape between the wings and fuselage?
8. Why do you normally apply rudder when applying aileron?
9. How can gliders stall at higher speeds?
10. Why does a glider spin?
11. What is the purpose of a glider's fin?
12. What is the purpose of a tail-plane?
13. How does an elevator work? What is the effect on stability of reducing the cockpit load?
14. What is the effect on stability of reducing the cockpit load?
15. Why is the best glide angle given by the tangent to the polar curve?
16. If you bank a glider, its stall speed increases. Why then is it safer to make a well banked final turn?

AIRCRAFT STRUCTURE AND INTEGRITY

Introduction
Pilots cannot all be engineers but they should know enough to determine whether their aircraft is safe to fly. An aircraft will almost inevitably incur some damage, even if very minor, as well as normal wear and tear through use. An understanding of the structure of the aircraft is therefore essential to knowing whether an aircraft is safe to fly when it is inspected each day. While in flight, it is also essential to know the maximum stresses that a glider can safely incur.

Fibrous materials
In many aircraft structures the length of a component is often much larger than its width or height. An obvious example is the wing spar that runs the length of the wings. Designers therefore choose materials that are particularly strong in specific directions, so that their weights are efficient when compared to their strength.

The preferred materials are composed of thin, flexible, long fibres which are strong when they are pulled (known as strength in tension). However aircraft can go both up & down and left & right, and so many components have to be strong in at least two directions. The materials chosen must therefore be also strong when they are pushed and this is known as strength in compression. For example, a fibre such as steel wire is good in tension but will just flop about if you try to stand it on end. It has insufficient strength in compression even to support its own weight.

In order to create strength in compression in a fibrous material, the fibres have to be bonded together somehow. The fibres can then help each other not to buckle when compressed. The "glue" or resin is usually a softer, lighter material which distributes and transfers the load within the structure so that each reinforcing fibre carries a proportional share of the load.

Wood
Wood is a fibrous material that has evolved to support the weight of trees. It is also an excellent material for building gliders because the cellulose fibres are strong in tension and are bonded by a matrix of lignin which resists compression.

In choosing the right wood, for example for a wooden spar, the engineer must select wood with the right rate of growth to get the right proportion of fibre to resin. The spacing of the grain of the wood indicates this.

However it is very difficult to find a long enough piece of wood that had exactly the right characteristics along its length to be a wing spar. Consequently most spars are laminated, ie there are several different pieces of wood bonded together to get the required strength without too much of a weight penalty.

The wing is then built with a traditional skeleton structure. The backbone of the wing is the spar that runs along its length. Running parallel to the spar are stringers and running across the spar and stringers are ribs that are shaped to give the wing its aerofoil section. This basic structure is then covered with fabric.

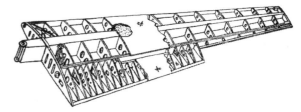

Traditional spar and ribs

Some aircraft structures are two-dimensional (length and width are large with respect to thickness). Plywood is often used for such structures. Several thin boards (plies) are glued together so that the fibres of the various layers cross over at different angles (usually 90 degrees)

Metal
Whole gliders are made of metal. The best known examples are the venerable Blaniks which have been in common use. Other gliders such as K13s also use extensive metal parts in addition to wood. This is because metals are strong in both tension and compression and so they can be used for one-dimensional components and in as sheets for two-dimensional structures. As a rule of thumb, aluminium is three times heavier, but also three times stronger than wood.

Although aluminium is an element, it is rarely available with 100% purity. It is available as different grades and is often mixed with other metals to create alloys. For aviation use a report accompanies a shipment that guarantees the chemical and physical properties.

Although steel is three times stronger than aluminium, it is also three times heavier. Consequently steel is used sparingly, and only in applications where its hardness is essential. Mild steel is used for items that need little strength, but elsewhere higher performance materials are used containing chromium and molybdenum for vital parts such as the main pins and other wing fittings.

A tube shape can provide the necessary strength without the centre of the tube being filled. These tubes can be welded together to produce strong structures. However steel is not used in sheets like aluminium or plywood because it would be too thin to achieve a nice finish. That is why the steel fuselage in a K13 uses tubes in a criss-cross shape to carry the forces in compression or tension and the whole structure is then covered with a light-weight fabric to give it the required aerodynamic shape.

Composite materials

Like wood, composite materials are fibrous. However they have several big advantages. The transfer of stress from fibre to fibre is through chemical bonding and so the material is stronger, stiffer for a given weight. It also has a longer life because of its high resistance to corrosion and damp.

The designer can use fibres in the right direction exactly where the stresses will occur and in precisely the amount required. Like wood, the fibres are embedded in a resin to hold them in place and this provides the required support against buckling. Sometimes the fibres are embedded in resin in long straight lines, for example in the wing spars, but elsewhere the fibres used in fabrics which provide strength in two directions like plywood.

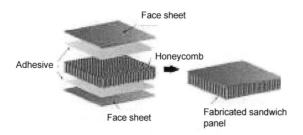

Unlike sheets of plywood or metal which can only be curved in a single direction, composite materials using cloth allow double curvature and smooth shapes. These complex shapes are essential to achieve the ultimate in aerodynamic performance.

The fibres in composite materials can be glass, nylon, Kevlar, carbon and polyethylene. For their weight these are strong, but as a cloth for two dimensional structures they have little stiffness. This is overcome by creating thicker areas to provide reinforcement, or more recently by building a sandwich structures in which the composite layers are held apart by a lightweight core (foam or "honeycomb"). In early glass gliders such as some Kestrels this core was balsa wood.

Building a composite glider

Each major component of composite glider is built as two parts in moulds. The moulds are built to extremely high precision and therefore very expensive. The outer coating of the glider is applied first and then the inner layers are systematically added. Strict quality control is needed to ensure that each layer is correctly oriented and bonded. Once the items such as the spars and control rods have been inserted, the two halves of each wing, tail-plane and fuselage are then joined. The whole component is then "cured" under controlled conditions of temperature and humidity to ensure that the resin has set.

Even if the moulds have been well designed, the outside of the structure then needs a great deal of work to produce the smooth and shiny finish.

Such is the strength of composites that much of the structure of wooden wings (the ribs and stringers) is not needed.

Undercarriage

A stall at as little as 10 feet over an asphalt runway with the gear up can lead to severe injury. The nature of the runway surface has little effect. Even on grass, the impact is only perhaps 2% less. If, however, the gear is down and locked, there should be usually no injury to the pilot in this situation. The main wheel and its support will probably be damaged because the springs (if any) will not sustain the impact of a hard "pancake" landing, but then the energy is further absorbed by the bending of the gear support tubing.

Aircraft structure and integrity

The manual of some older gliders even suggest landing gear up on a ploughed field to prevent expensive damage to the landing gear. However this increases the risk to your much more valuable spine. Never land gear up.

Unserviceable gliders

If you become aware or suspect that a glider has become unserviceable, you must ensure that the aircraft does not fly again until it has been checked by a qualified inspector. The owner should also be informed.

If you or anyone else has written in a daily inspection book that a glider is unserviceable, then it needs a qualified inspector to release the aircraft back into service, even if you think the problem has been fixed.

If there is an engineering fault, ie not caused by an accident, a gliding inspector will decide if it merits reporting more widely, in case it occurs elsewhere.

Accidents

If the glider has been damaged between the times of you getting in and out, the event is classified as an accident. This must be reported this to the BGA, and the owner. You will not be reprimanded because safety is paramount. The objective of any de-brief is to learn from mistakes and to repair damage as quickly as possible. If someone is injured while flying the aircraft that you knew was damaged, but you had not reported this, you could be held responsible.

Events when damage occurred with no-one on board or when an accident almost happened are classified as "incidents". These must also be reported to the BGA.

All accidents and all incidents which caused or might have caused injury to persons or damage to aircraft must be reported on the BGA's accident form within one month of the occurrence.

Serious accidents must be reported as soon as possible to the Police and the Department of Transport Air Accident Investigation Board. They must also be reported to the BGA with 24 hours. Your CFI will normally arrange this.

Serious accidents are defined as those resulting in death, serious injury or substantial damage to any aircraft. Substantial damage is defined as "adversely

affecting the structural strength, performance or flight characteristics of the aircraft, and would normally require major repair or replacement of the affected component". The aircraft must not be moved without the permission of the AAIB other than to extract persons or valuables and to avoid damage by fire or danger to the public or others.

Airworthiness

Airworthiness is subject to a European regulatory process, called Part M. The CAA is responsible for interpreting and applying EASA's regulation but allows the BGA to deliver and manage the airworthiness function through its inspectors. However, most importantly, the owner has the responsibility for ensuring that the glider is airworthy.

Annual inspection

Airworthiness of EASA sailplanes registered in the UK is overseen by the BGA which is known as a 'Continuing Airworthiness Management Organisation' (CAMO).

Part M covers all aircraft, with the exception of some experimental aircraft and some ancient types, known as Annex 2 gliders. Apart from these exceptions, all aircraft types are issued with a non-expiring EASA Certificate of Airworthiness (CofA). For aircraft that are part of the BGA organisation, this is validated annually with an Airworthiness Review Certificate (ARC) by an authorised signatory, ie a BGA inspector.

Part M states that the ARC (which cannot be replaced cheaply) should be carried in the glider. A laminated photocopy might be useful here.

Any aircraft may be selected for audit either by the CAA or by the BGA Quality Dept.. You may also be asked at random to supply a copy of your insurance certificate.

If you use a CAMO other than the BGA or your BGA ARC has expired more than three months, to retain access to BGA inspectors you will need to purchase an Airworthiness Support Package, but I need not go into this further in this book.

Pilot maintenance

You can perform your own maintenance on your glider, but only as described in the Glider Maintenance Schedule (GMS) and in BGA's

Airworthiness Maintenance Procedure 2-1 booklet on its web-site. There is the list of tasks (known as 'Pilot Owner Maintenance') that qualified pilots (Bronze Badge qualified) are authorised to carry out under Part M. Pilot owner maintenance has to be signed for in the glider logbook by the pilot owner. Maintenance outside the scope of 'Pilot Owner Maintenance' has to be signed for by an inspector.

The list of allowed pilot-owner maintenance tasks can be summarised as including the following:
- The simple visual inspections or operations to check for general condition and obvious damage and normal operation of the airframe, engines, systems and components.

And excluding
- Critically safety related, whose incorrect performance will drastically affect the airworthiness of the aircraft or flight safety
- Requires the removal of major components or major assembly unless otherwise specified in the flight manual as a pilot task
- Anything carried out in compliance with an Airworthiness Directive or an Airworthiness Limitation Item, unless specifically allowed
- Requires the use of special tools, calibrated tools (except torque wrench and crimping tool) and/or requires the use of test equipment or special testing such as non-destructive testing
- Any unscheduled special inspections (e.g. heavy landing, ground loop or similar checks
- Systems essential for IFR operations
- Anything listed as a complex maintenance task ie a major repair, or a repair a component such as an instrument

Any task described in the aircraft flight manual as preparing the aircraft for flight such as assembling the glider wings or pre-flight checks, does not require a Certificate of Release to Service.

Details of modifications, repairs, replacements and inspections must be entered into the glider's log book by the inspector. Modifications to all gliders now require approval by the CAA, a design organisation or the manufacturer. For example, clamping a home-made camera mount to a wing is no longer legal without approval.

If you wish carry out the work yourself (after determining it is within your capability), you must discuss it with your BGA inspector before starting the work, so that an appropriate level of supervision can be maintained.

Rigging and daily inspection
A glider must be inspected each day before flying. This includes a positive control check if there are manually connected controls. You should be cleared by the CFI or someone deputed by the CFI to perform a daily inspection on each type of glider. A positive control check must also be done after rigging a glider. A note of both the rigging and the independent control check should be made in the DI book.

Any newly-rigged BGA club aircraft or any BGA club glider which has been subject to adjustment or repair since its last flight, must be first flown by a pilot approved by the CFI or his deputy for that purpose.

Standard daily inspection checklist
To do a DI, the pilot must be 'qualified'. Under EASA rules, a qualified pilot is someone who has a licence and until we move to a standardised licensing scheme, this means a Bronze Badge. However the CFI can authorise someone without a licence.

The BGA has published a standard checklist for the daily inspection (DI). Some tasks may not be applicable depending on the glider type, equipment installed and previous use. This DI is assuming that the aircraft has been rigged before flight and items such as batteries have already been installed.

General
- Remove frost, ice, snow or water if present.
- Ensure that the interior of the aircraft is reasonably clean and free of clutter and rubbish.
- Ensure that all loose equipment is correctly stowed and accounted for
- Review DI book or Technical Log to ensure previously reported defects are addressed
- Review the Aircraft Flight Manual for any specific inspection tasks.

Wings
- Inspect skin/covering, flying controls, struts, fairing for obvious defects, damage and security
- Inspect fitment and locking of main de-rigging points
- Inspect fitment and locking of flying controls and wing extension connections

Aircraft structure and integrity

- Flying control cables and controls rods as visible for tension or operation
- Inspect condition of wing joint sealing tape
- Check water ballast drains for correct operation
- Check drain holes clear
- Inspect tip wheel/skid for damage, security and operation.

Fuselage & empennage
- Inspect skin/covering, flying controls, struts for obvious defects, damage and security
- Inspect fitment and locking of tail de-rigging points
- Check water ballast drains for correct operation
- Check drain holes and static vents clear
- Check Pitot/static ports and total energy probes for damage, security and ports clear
- Check release hook(s) for damage and security. Carry out function check, including back release.

Landing gear
- Inspect main, nose/tail wheels and tyres for wear, security, damage, correct extension, inflation and tyre creep
- Inspect wheel brake for leakage and condition and fluid level
- Check operation of wheel brake
- Inspect main/tail skid for damage and security

Cabin
- Check flying controls for operation and sense. Perform positive control check
- Check flying control bungee springs for damage, misalignment and security
- Check seat, rudder pedal and any other adjustable control for operation and locking
- Check battery is charged, correctly located and secure and connections are tight
- Check instruments for readings consistent with ambient conditions
- Check navigation and soaring equipment as appropriate
- Inspect seat(s) and harnesses. Check operation of harness release buckle
- Check cushions including energy absorbing cushions for condition and security

- Check oxygen quantity for intended flight is sufficient and bottle is secure. Check mask is clean and secure
- Check all markings and loading placards are present and legible
- Check for correct ballast weights properly installed and secured.

Canopy
- Check canopy for damage, security and cleanliness
- Clean canopy if necessary. Wash using a soft cloth, not a paper towel
- Inspect jettison controls for inadvertent operation
- Check direct vision panel for operation and cleanliness
- Check wool "string" is present and is in a satisfactory condition

Powerplant
- With engine raised or cowlings open, inspect engine, accessories and engine bay as visible for damage, security, and signs of overheating or leaks
- Inspect propeller blades, hub and folding device for damage and security
- Check engine controls and switches, carry out the self-test if installed
- Check lubricating or additive oil quantity
- Check fuel tank water drain
- Check sufficient fuel quantity of correct grade/mix for intended flight. Filler cap tight
- Check fuel filter if external inspection is possible
- Check coolant level
- Inspect air intake and filters.
- Inspect exhaust system for damage, security and evidence of leaks
- Retract engine or close cowlings and check secure.

Personal equipment
- Check parachute for condition, signs of tampering and packing date expiry.
- Check GPS, Barograph or flight logger is on board aircraft and serviceable.
- Check drinking water, hat, gloves, maps & charts, task details etc.
- Check personal relief bottle/tube/bag is ready for use.
- Water ballast loaded and balanced

Is it broken?

One of the most difficult things when inspecting a glider, even for experts, is deciding whether a glider is broken. The incident itself is not always a good guide. An apparently minor ground loop can do much damage, whereas a more spectacular rotation may not cause any damage at all.

Some aircraft are more durable than others. A fairly heavy landing in some gliders will produce no damage, but will be serious in other types such as the Astir.

The main places to check in a DI are around the undercarriage, under the seat (if accessible), the rear fuselage around the fin, and all hinges of control surfaces. The hinges of the rudder are susceptible to damage from incorrect spin recovery.

Most often there will be little easily visible damage after an accident. The first step is just cleaning the area because mud and dead flies can obscure a problem. Even then various optical devices may still be needed to inspect hidden places, and even holes may have to be cut.

Hinges are often hidden by Mylar. Broken pushrod guides and un-bonded wing ribs may also appear undamaged to superficial inspection. In short, if you have any doubts at all, get someone who knows the type to give the aircraft a thorough inspection.

Any pilot exceeding the 'g' loading permitted by the glider's flight manual should report this and the aircraft should not be flown again until it has been inspected and a log book entry made and signed by an approved inspector.

Every repair needs a thorough assessment by a qualified engineer and, if it is not in the manual, a repair scheme that is approved by the factory.

Wear and tear

As far as strength is concerned, the major components of a glider will last for its life, but wear and tear from regular usage will have an effect on its surface and fittings. Each part may develop 'play', ie it can be waggled and it will shift slightly. This can affect the control surfaces, the tail-plane, undercarriage and the wings. These aspects are all checked at each annual inspection, but it is still important to check for this daily.

Nuts can work loose due to the vibration of the aircraft, and so they must have some form of a locking device to keep them in place. The most common ways of locking are by using self-locking nuts, lock-washers, and safety wire. Self-locking nuts have a fibre or plastic insert. Lock-washers are often jagged star-shaped objects but sometimes they are just look like a split washer. When safety wire is used, it is usually stainless steel or brass, and not just any piece of wire that happens to be lying around. Wing nuts are only used for non-critical applications where something such as a battery has to be removed frequently.

Seat-belts and control wires can fray, while other metal things whilst not structural can simply corrode. Almost everything in a glider is there for a purpose. If it broken or loose, then it needs to be fixed.

More than any other area on the glider, the wheel-well and landing gear probably receives more punishment due to mud, water, gravel, and other flying debris. As well as checking tyre pressure and the wheel brake, always give a good general inspection to this area.

The surface of the glider will also deteriorate, especially if it is parked for long period in sunshine, or if it is frozen, especially after it has been allowed to get damp. This is because water expands when it freezes so any small gaps can increase markedly. Consequently the change to low temperatures at high altitude can damage surfaces.

Pre-flight checks

If you haven't done the DI, it is still a good idea to walk round any aircraft that you are about to fly. There have been many instances of unreported damage where other pilots have unwittingly flown the aircraft subsequently.

Even after doing the DI, you are not still ready to take off.

- Have you satisfied yourself about the weather during your flight?
- Are any NOTAMs applicable throughout your route or will other significant activities take place at the airfield while you are airborne?
- Have you removed the tail dolly?
- You must also brief anyone else with whom you are flying about the security (jettisoning the canopy, the seat straps, how to use a parachute, not to touch the controls and the purpose of the flight.)

Aircraft structure and integrity

- The standard CB SIFT CBE check would be then appropriate.

Looking after a glider

If you are washing a glider, ensure that the airbrakes are locked shut. The water could collect in the well and freeze in flight.

Take care not to get water into orifices such as the static vents. This will disable some instruments. A hose will be particularly effective at forcing in water. Just use a bucket and sponge.

Always wash a canopy with water before polishing it. Unless dirt is removed first, you may scratch the *Perspex®*. Canopies are particularly fragile when they are cold. Trying to lock a canopy, when there is a seat-strap hanging out, can crack it. Unlocked canopies can fly open in strong winds, and the resulting stress will crack them.

Moisture and solar radiation are particularly detrimental to glass-fibre structures. Regular waxing helps, but it only delays the inevitable deterioration. Wooden gliders should not be left out because moisture will degrade the wood. All gliders should therefore be put away if they are not being used.

Airframe log books

The CAA Airframe Log Book is CAP398 and it has a blue cover. On the white pages you should enter:
1. Date
2. No of flights. (Unless your club/syndicate partner requires it or your airframe is flight cycle limited, it is not necessary to record the number of flights.)
3. Flight time. The total for the day in hours and minutes, or hours and decimal hours showing clearly which method is being used.
4. Total since manufacture. This is the cumulative total airframe time
5. Engine cycles. Only required this affects your engine's time between overhauls
6. Particulars of maintenance and other work. You should record maintenance checks, mandatory inspections, modifications etc. (Records of the serial numbers of components taken off and put on, and the release number of parts used; may be contained in a file provided a reference is made. In addition, any "Pilot Maintenance" should be certified in this section.
7. Signature, Authority, Date. If you have used column six for other than pilot maintenance,

you should sign this section and enter your authorisation number to release the aircraft to service. Pilot maintenance should not be certified in this section.

Flight limitations

The manoeuvring 'envelope' of a glider can be depicted by a graph showing the minimum and maximum speeds that are allowable under different g loadings. The envelope is the shaded area in the

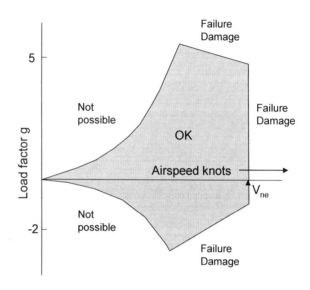

diagram above and shows the limits within which the glider is structurally safe. The envelope is usually drawn using maximum speeds and maximum g that were calculated for the design of the glider. The upper curve (the 'stall line') shows how the stall speed increases with increasing g. It is either physically impossible to enter the areas outside the envelope or it is positively dangerous.

Maximum load factors are typically +5.3g to -2.65g at manoeuvring speed V_A (see later). However it is important to realise that the placard in the glider only gives the major limitations and that almost all gliders have the maximum load reduced to 3.5g when the airbrakes are open and to allow for gusts.

Maximum speeds

The maximum speeds are displayed on a placard in every glider. V_{NE} is the speed that should never be exceeded, and should be self-explanatory. However, above V_{NE} is another speed V_D, the design dive speed. It is not shown on the placard because it is the theoretical speed used in calculating the structure and materials of the glider. V_{NE} is usually set at 90% of V_D to allow for gusts.

Your glider should never have flown at V_D, but at least once when it was in pristine condition on a test flight in ideal conditions, it was taken up to 95% of V_D by an expert. Remember that many of the forces on a glider increase with the square of the speed and that 5% above V_{NE} is only a few extra knots. Consequently if you exceed V_{NE} even slightly, you are taking on the risks of a test pilot. If you are flying near V_{NE}, do not use more than one third deflection on any control to avoid overstressing.

The glider's placard also shows the maximum manoeuvring speed and the maximum speeds for the winch, aerotow, with positive flap and with the undercarriage down. The maximum manoeuvring speed V_A is the speed below which it is safe to use full deflection of any one control without damaging the glider. This is normally 2.25 times the normal stalling speed. It is often set at the same speed as the maximum rough air-speed (V_B), though not necessarily. A glider designed under JAR-22 must be able to withstand vertical gusts of 30kt when flying at V_B but don't fly any faster in very rough air and do not do aerobatics in rough air.

The maximum aerotow speed is also often set at the same speed as V_A, because full control deflections are sometimes needed to stay behind the tug in rough conditions. The maximum undercarriage speed is usually set at a speed to ensure the undercarriage doors remain attached.

Tail-slides

If you ever find yourself pointing almost straight upwards with very little air-speed, the glider may move backwards. There is a risk that the control surfaces will be damaged by the reversed air flow, and so you should centralise the controls, push both feet hard against the rudder pedals and hold the stick firmly.

Forces during a winch-launch

During a wire launch an additional force is added to the usual three forces. This is the tension on the wire. At the top of the launch, the tension acts mainly downwards, almost like pulling additional 'g', except that only the glider experiences this force, not the occupants. A high-speed launch coupled with this high loading could place the glider near the

edge of the envelope. A maximum winch/auto-tow speed is therefore defined for each glider.

The glider is also protected from excess loads during a wire launch by the weak link, but gusts on the glider near the limits could overstress it before the weak link broke. The black weak link that is used to launch heavy two-seaters breaks at 2200 pounds, but the weak links required for other gliders can be half this value. Using the wrong link could, therefore, allow a glider to sustain an excessive load of which the pilot would be unaware, unless a structural failure occurred.

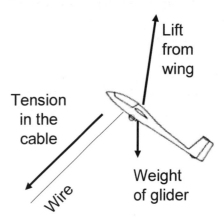

The correct weak link tends to fail at about twice the stalling speed.

Weight in the cockpit

Ballast limits are carefully calculated for every individual glider and change over time, especially after a repair. The loading limitations calculated at an inspection for the ARC therefore override whatever is in the flight manual of the glider.

The distance between the centre of lift and the centre of gravity greatly affects the stability of the glider. Insufficient weight in the cockpit, especially in the front seat, moves the centre of gravity back and is therefore exceptionally dangerous because it makes it difficult to recover from a stall or spin.

Use well-secured, additional weights to achieve the correct ballast. For inexperienced solo pilots the minimum cockpit weight should be exceeded by 15Kg (33 pounds).

You should also not fly above the weight limit. Trimming the aircraft becomes impossible, and high-g manoeuvres will amplify the excess weight placing undue stress on the glider. At high speeds excess weight also puts an undue strain on the tail-plane, though a failure is unlikely.

Summary

Much of this chapter is useful to ensuring a glider is safe to fly but the following points are essential:

- If in doubt, get it inspected
- Always do a DI and have a good look round even if someone else did the DI
- Read the flight manual before you fly any glider
- Understand what the various maximum speeds mean
- Pay attention to cockpit loading especially if you are light
- Understand why there is a minimum speed and a maximum speed on a winch-launch
- Understand the effect of winch-launching with the wrong weak link

Questions

1. What name is given to the maximum speed at which it is safe to use full deflection of any one control without damaging the glider?
2. What is the maximum air-speed and maximum manoeuvring speed of the glider that you normally fly? (You may have to look this up in the flight manual.)
3. What is the name given to the certificate that shows the glider has passed its annual inspection?
4. You were sitting in the cockpit ready to launch when someone drove over your wing-tip. Is this a reportable accident and, if so, to whom?
5. Your glider's radio is broken. Are you as pilot with a Bronze Badge allowed to take it out and send it for repair?

INSTRUMENTATION

Introduction
In an emergency, an experienced pilot could fly most gliders without any instrumentation. Height above the ground can be judged by eye and even air-speed can be judged by ear especially if the glider is not well sealed, but accurate instruments make flying much easier, safer and legal. In this chapter the most common objects on the panel are described.

Minimum instrumentation
Under EASA regulations gliders must be equipped with:
- An air-speed indicator
- A sensitive altimeter

If the glider has an engine, it must also have a compass, but you would be well advised to fit one in any case, and to have an accurate time-piece. (Compasses are discussed in the Navigation chapter.) Any additional instruments specified by the glider's manufacturer, such as an outside air temperature gauge must also be fitted.

Air-speed indicator
The air-speed indicator (ASI) measures the pressure caused by the air flowing into a forward facing tube, the 'Pitot tube'. This dynamic pressure is compared with the normal pressure measured at static vents, which are not facing the air-flow.

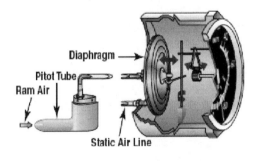

A typical ASI

The comparison is done by a diaphragm inside an enclosed container. The air on one side of the diaphragm is at the static pressure, and the other at the dynamic pressure. A lever arrangement links the movement of the diaphragm to the needle. On British gliders the scale is in knots (nautical miles per hour).

The Pitot is usually in the nose of the glider. The static ports are also located on the exterior of the aircraft, but at a location, such as the side, chosen to detect the prevailing atmospheric pressure as accurately as possible with the minimum disturbance from the movement of the aircraft itself.

On the dial of the ASI there are often two coloured bands. The green band runs from 1.1 times the stall speed (at maximum weight with the flaps in neutral and the landing gear up) to the maximum manoeuvring speed and the yellow band runs from the maximum manoeuvring speed to V_{NE}.

There may also be a white arc up to maximum speed allowable for positive flaps. A yellow triangle will show the lowest approach speed (at maximum weight without water ballast) recommended by the manufacturer.

ASIs are usually accurate if properly installed. They have to be correct within 2 knots to well beyond V_{ne} to pass the CoA. However there are a few reasons why an ASI could mis-read. The most likely reason is that you are not flying straight. If the air arrives at an angle, it cannot fully flow down the Pitot tube. The dynamic pressure measured by the ASI will be reduced, and it will under-read. However, ASIs can also mis-read because of water or ice blocking the Pitot tube or the static vent. This may happen when flying in cloud and/or at great altitude.

On some aircraft it is difficult to find the right position for the static vent and so there is sometimes a small error. The ASI must be calibrated to allow for this. Usually the adjustment increases the indicated air-speed. There is also another small error if the air temperature at altitude is very different from the norm.

However at height the reduced air pressure causes another, bigger error in the ASI. Where the atmosphere has a lower pressure, the dynamic pressure experienced by the Pitot tube will also be reduced, and so the ASI will under-read.

As a rough approximation, to get the true air-speed you add 2% per 1000 feet of altitude to indicated air-speed. So if you think you are flying at 100 knots at 10,000' altitude, your true airspeed is about 120 knots.

Although many of the stresses on a glider are lessened in the thinner air at altitude, some effects, such as flutter on the control surfaces, are directly affected by air-speed whatever the air pressure. If you fly fast at altitude, you must be aware of this limitation of the ASI. In summary:

> **Indicated airspeed is often less than true airspeed**

Altimeter

In an earlier chapter the altimeter was described as a barometer, though in reality it is more sophisticated. The sensitive version that is used in aviation was invented by Paul Kollsman in 1928.

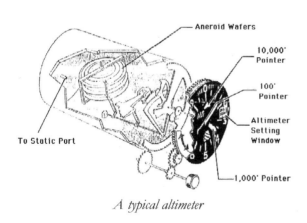

A typical altimeter

A stack of sealed aneroid wafers comprises the main component of the altimeter. (Aneroid means 'no liquid'.) These wafers expand and contract with changes in atmospheric pressure from the static source. The mechanical linkage translates these changes into pointer movements on the indicator. Commonly, altimeters have three pointers, as in the diagram. It is quite easy to mis-read the pointers, and so a few altimeters replace or supplement the pointers with counters.

The main error is caused by the lag in the altimeter reading as the glider climbs and descends.

Variometers and probes

A variometer is primarily a vertical speed indicator. All variometers (varios) measure the rate of climb and descent by measuring the rate of change of air pressure. Many measure the flow in and out of an insulated flask of air.

The flows are small and so the instrument is highly sensitive to small effects. For example, the insulation of the flask is there to minimise errors from air flows caused by temperature changes. To ensure the air in the tubing from the flask is not greatly affected by temperature, the flask is usually mounted near the vario keeping the amount of un-insulated tubing short.

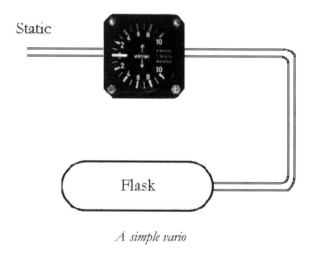

A simple vario

Errors could also arise from the positioning of the static port. If there were just one static port, the vario would give a false reading when the glider yawed because the increased pressure from the air impinging on one side. This is overcome by having interconnected static ports on both sides of the fuselage. Consequently the resulting pressure from this static is a steady average.

If you trade off some speed in a glider and climb, you do not want this gain in altitude to be registered by the vario as a thermal. All varios should therefore be connected to compensation devices that subtract the effects of changing air-speed, so that they only measure the effect of the rising air. This is normally done by using a total energy probe that creates additional suction in the vario system as the air-speed increases, though other variations in the plumbing and electronic compensation are sometimes used. Completely spurious vario readings are often caused by forgetting to install the total energy probe after rigging. However vario errors can also be caused by leaks in tubing and joints and by moisture in the tubing.

Electronic varios also measure the flow of air, but because there are no moving parts, they can respond more sensitively and quickly than mechanical varios. To avoid them become impossibly jittery, some form of mechanical or electronic 'damping' is necessary.

As the glider flies into lift, it will take time to acquire a vertical speed because a considerable weight must be accelerated upwards. This is the main cause in the lag between the arrival in lift and its indication by any type of variometer.

Each make of vario has its own features and so it is worth studying the manual carefully. You will encounter some terminology. 'Total energy' means that the variometer shows the glider's actual climb rate. 'Netto' means that the vario shows the air-mass movement, not what the glider is achieving. 'Supernetto' and 'relative' both mean the same thing. They are the rate of climb that you would achieve if you slowed down to thermalling speed.

In the UK varios usually show knots, ie 1 nautical mile per hour. A nautical mile is 6,080 feet and so one knot is almost exactly 100 feet per minute. It is also quite close to 0.5 metres per second.

Staring at the variometer when you are thermalling means that you are not looking out properly. The BGA recommends that all gliders should be equipped with audio variometers and that pilots should be trained in their use.

A useful feature in a vario is an 'averager'. This will give a better indication of the rate of climb during a complete circle. One often hears pilots claiming to be a 'four-knotter', when what they probably mean is that the vario occasionally peaks at this reading. The averager will show whether the achieved rate of climb really is good enough to stay with, or whether it might be better to find a better thermal.

Another feature in many varios is a MacCready setting. This enables the pilot to fly at the optimal speed at all times. The device may be a simple ring around the dial or it may be electronic. The pilot inputs the average rate of climb for the minimum acceptable thermal and can then read off the speed to fly in either lift or sink. However many pilots say that slavishly reacting to every small fluctuation in the recommended speed is the quickest way to feel air-sick.

Turn & slip indicator and artificial horizon
The turn & slip indicator (also called the turn & bank) shows whether the glider is turning and whether it is pointing straight at the airflow. The rate of turn is measured by a gyroscope. The amount of slip is shown by either a pendulum or a heavy ball mounted in a curved sealed glass tube. This senses the side force in an uncoordinated turn.

A typical turn & slip indicator

However the is instrument does not show the pitch of the aircraft. A pilot who is flying blind must therefore also use the air-speed indicator to keep the glider's nose pointing somewhere near the horizon. Interpreting two instruments at the same time increases the work-load greatly.

The artificial horizon is another gyroscopic instrument. This combines both bank and pitch indication on one display. The horizon is usually represented as the boundary between a blue top half of a sphere and the brown or green bottom half. The pilot merely has to imagine that he is looking at the real horizon to maintain a steady pitch and bank.

A typical artificial horizon

Both of these instruments rely on gyroscopes that are driven by electric motors. These take time to speed up. Until that happens they must not be relied upon. A small flag showing "off" (see picture above) shows when the artificial horizon is not yet fully functioning.

Some artificial horizons can only tolerate a specific range of bank angles. If the aircraft rolls too steeply, the attitude indicator can "tumble" and become temporarily unusable. For this reason, some devices are fitted with a "cage" to restore the gyroscope to an erect position.

Transponders

Transponders receive 'interrogations' from radars on a radio frequency at each sweep of the radar head. The transponders then send corresponding 'replies' back on another frequency. Older devices use Mode A and Mode C. These send back a four-digit identity code that the pilot has dialled in and, in the case of Mode C, an automatic pressure-altitude report. Replies from transponders are known as 'squawks' and are used to display the altitude and identity of aircraft on controllers' radar displays.

A Filser transponder

These old technologies are being replaced by Mode Select (Mode S). The limitations of the four digit code and several other capacity constraints are removed. Mode S radars can interrogate transponders selectively and receive individual replies. This means unambiguous identification of aircraft, improved tracking and a significant reduction in interference and on the loading on the reply radio frequency. Pressure-altitude information is provided to an accuracy of 25 feet, but the radar itself works out where the aircraft is horizontally. Even Mode S transponders do not broadcast GPS

positions, though an additional technology called ADS-B, uses GPS.

It seems probable at the time of writing that powered aircraft will soon need Mode S transponders to pass through controlled airspace (classes A-E). Gliders may be exempted for a while, but the chances of getting clearance through airspace without a transponder will probably reduce.

In addition to airspace of Classes A-E, the CAA wishes to introduce transponder mandatory zones. In these zones, flight will only be possible with a transponder. The extent of these zones is currently the subject of debate.

GPS

The most familiar satellite navigation system in the UK uses the US Department of Defense "Navstar" Global Positioning System or GPS.

The receiver relies on maintaining line of sight between itself and several satellites. If there is interference, insufficient satellites may be 'visible'. Sometimes only a two-dimensional position will be available, ie no altitude.

The GPS system has generally been highly reliable, but it has been known to suffer technical and human failure. The satellite clock, which is at the heart of the system, may drift off time, the satellite may stray from its orbit or its transmitter may simply fail. It can take up to two hours for such errors to be resolved. At such times, position errors have been reported of up to 2 km.

A basic Garmin GPS unit

There are other sources of error such as high terrain, reflected signals, external interference/ jamming, sunspots and the whims of the US DoD. Consequently, GPS must not be relied upon as a sole navigation reference, ie you must still take a map in your glider and know how to use it.

Two GPS aerials close to each other can cause interference. No position at all may then be indicated or worse a wildly inaccurate position can be displayed.

Nevertheless, if the GPS display agrees with everything else you know from your map reading and general situational awareness, then the GPS display is likely to be providing the most accurate information.

More sophisticated devices using handheld computers or built into the variometer, will also provide additional information about the task, final glides, airspace and even which way to circle.

You should familiarise about the system while on the ground and have it set up properly in advance of the flight. Keying in information while in flight reduces your look-out time unacceptably and the work-load will cause errors. Recognize also that airspace information usually has not come directly from an official source and may be subject to errors and omissions.

Remember also that the most common errors are bad co-ordinates for a turn-point and mis-keying the coordinates. Never totally rely on a GPS and be prepared for the unexpected.

FLARM

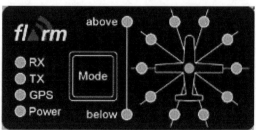

A FLARM display

FLARM is an entirely optional device for avoiding collisions. It works by broadcasting the aircraft's position and altitude that have been derived from a GPS receiver. The device only uses a low powered transmitter and so is less of a drain on batteries than a transponder.

A FLARM unit in another aircraft, usually within a range of 5 km can analyse the broadcast information and from changes in position over a few seconds, it can calculate the course of the hazard and decide if a collision is a possibility.

At first contact, an indicator lights up showing the approximate direction of the nearest aircraft. However if a collision is forecast as being a strong possibility, an alarm is sounded.

This device is popular in many European countries but has only gained partial acceptance in the UK to date. The arguments in its favour emphasise that it is a supplement to a good look-out, which is difficult to maintain with 100% reliability over a long flight. It is also easy to miss another aircraft against a varied background of mountain and forest. Those against believe their look-out is always adequate and feel that the expense is unnecessary. Some FLARM units are now approved loggers and this may improve the rate of acceptance in the UK.

Electrical terminology

A basic understanding of electricity is useful when operating a glider since several instruments use power from a battery.

Water is commonly used as the analogy when explaining the terminology. The quantity of water flowing down a pipe per second is similar to the quantity of electricity flowing per second in a wire. For electricity, this quantity known as the current, and it is measured in 'amperes', which is usually shortened to 'amps' and abbreviated to 'A'. A thousandth of an amp is a 'milliamp', and is usually written as 'mA'.

By increasing the pressure, you can deliver more water per second down the same pipe. For electricity, the pressure that squirts the current down a wire is known as the 'voltage', and this is measured in 'volts', and is abbreviated as 'V'.

The amount of energy passing down the wire each second depends on the quantity of current that is flowing and how hard it is being squirted. This rate of delivery of energy, known as power, is measured in 'watts'. Volts multiplied by amps equal watts.

$$V \times A = W$$

Instrumentation

Consequently an instrument using 10 watts at 12 volts is receiving current at the rate of 10/12 amps = 0.83 amps. Some instruments such as simple varios use little power, but devices such as artificial horizons use higher wattages, ie they will flatten the battery faster.

Lead-acid batteries

The normal rechargeable battery found in a glider gives out 12 - 13 volts. They contain concentrated sulphuric acid, which is highly corrosive. However the units are sealed and do not need to be topped up. They do not need to be kept upright in use, though they must not be charged inverted.

Some of the lead and acid is in the form of a paste that is lodged in holes in the main lead plates of the battery. The paste and the holes increase the effective surface area of the lead plates.

Glider batteries are 'deep cycle' batteries. This means they are designed to deliver energy over a long period, rather than the short burst of great energy needed to start a car. This makes them more sensitive than car batteries in terms of adverse reactions to over-voltage charging.

Recharging

Even though they are sealed, lead-acid batteries have valves to allow gas to escape. This may happen if high voltages are applied to the battery to charge it. If a battery charger that does not limit the current delivered to a deep-cycle battery, poor performance and premature failure is certain. For longer life, it is important to recharge batteries immediately after use and keep them fully charged over the winter. A discharged battery suffers something known as 'sulphation' which puts a coating on the lead plates and so degrades its ability to retain a charge. The ideal is continuous 'trickle' charging.

Not all the current delivered by the charger is stored by the battery. If the charger's output is 1 amp then a 7 ampere-hour battery will take about 7 x 1.75 hours to charge fully.

Discharging a lead-acid battery reduces the amount of lead on the plates and charging increases it again. However some of the paste is lost from the holes in the plates in each cycle. In fact sealed batteries are designed so that they are never fully charged. This stops gas being generated and so prevents the loss of fluid. However this part-charging also decreases the lives of these batteries compared with a car

battery. Gradually the battery delivers a lower voltage for a shorter and shorter period. Consequently some competition pilots even replace their batteries annually, though for most people this is excessive.

Other materials can be used in batteries. However using a different type of battery may be deemed to be a significant modification to the glider and may need official approval. Do not mix batteries using different technologies on the same circuit.

Lead, nickel and cadmium are all toxic metals. When the battery's performance has become unacceptable, do not just put them in the refuse, but take them for recycling.

Series and parallel

A 12-volt lead-acid battery is in fact six small batteries connected in series, known as 'cells', ie they are in a chain so that each battery steps up the voltage, until there is a difference of over 12 volts between the start of the series and the end. Connecting two 12-volt batteries in series would produce a sequence of 12 cells, ie about 25 volts. However, placing two 12-volt batteries side by side, known as 'in parallel', produces effectively one large 12 volt battery. In parallel both batteries must be in the same state of charge, otherwise one battery will try to recharge the other with a large current and so it may blow a fuse. For this reason do not try to charge two batteries on one charger.

Output

The normal brick-sized Yuasa NP7-12 12-volt glider battery will give out 7 ampere-hours when new. Although this implies one amp for seven hours, if used at this rate initially, the total output will not be at one amp at 12 volts for seven hours but will tail off over a longer period instead. Fortunately many instruments will continue to operate at lower voltages, but there will come a point when they will cease to function reliably. A voltmeter on the instrument panel is useful for seeing when to switch to another battery in flight.

Fuses

12 or 13 volts is a safe voltage. However this does not mean that a glider's battery cannot cause you safety problems.

Firstly lead-acid batteries are heavy and so must be well secured in the glider. Furthermore, connecting the two terminals of a battery together, even briefly, can allow a massive current to flow. The heat created by this 'short circuit' could start a fire, or gassing from the battery with perhaps even a spray of acid.

A fuse is a delicate piece of wire that burns out when an excessive current passes through it. To protect against short circuits, fuses are inserted into the wiring of a glider, one as close as possible to the positive terminal of each battery. Individual instruments will often have their own fuses in addition to the main fuses near the batteries. If the right fuse is chosen for each application, it will blow before a big enough current can pass that could damage an instrument.

(Incidentally for mains electricity, fuses just protect against fire. Only circuit breakers, known as residual current devices, can react fast enough to protect against electrocution.)

It is also helpful to be able to switch off any single instrument if there is a problem. The other instruments would then still be available.

Let us say that a radio consumes 150mA while on standby, but 1.8A during transmissions. Although it will only draw a big current for a short period, the fuse should be rated at not less than about 2 amps. If you were to use a lesser fuse, it would blow as soon as you pressed the transmit button. However, if you were to use a much more highly rated fuse, say 13 amps, and a fault were to develop, a high current could pass before the fuse blew. The consequence could be expensive damage to the radio, were a fault to develop.

DC and AC

Batteries deliver what is known as 'direct current', or DC. This means that the current flows steadily in the same direction and it is suitable for radios, computers and varios. However the electric motors that sometimes drive the gyroscopes in artificial horizons and in turn-and-slip indicators use a form of current, known as 'alternating current', or AC. This means that the current reverses its flow rapidly. To get an alternating current from DC, a device known as an 'inverter' is used. Sometime it is a separate box; sometimes it is built into the instrument.

Questions

1. What effect will altitude have on the indicated air-speed?
2. What property of the air is a variometer measuring?
3. What do the green and yellow bands on some ASIs mean?
4. What does a total energy probe do?
5. What type of variometer is recommended by the BGA?
6. If the Pitot tube is blocked with water or ice, will the ASI over-read or under-read?

WEATHER

Introduction

There are whole books that cover meteorology for pilots, and so another one has not been attempted here. Instead this chapter provides an outline of the subject emphasising where if affects gliding. Note that the weather is not a simple subject, so words like 'often' and 'usually' have been used liberally.

THE BASICS ABOUT THE WEATHER

Heat and temperature

Heat and temperature can be confused. Although people complain of the heat on a hot day, they are really complaining about the temperature. Heat is energy that can be spread thinly over a large volume, or it can be concentrated in a small volume. Some heat put into small volume will produce a greater temperature than if the same amount of heat were put into a larger volume. For example, a parcel of air at altitude will be cooler than the same parcel of air near the ground because the air will have expanded because of the lower pressure, and so its heat will be spread over a larger volume.

Heating by the sun

Cloudless air is effectively transparent, so that virtually none of the sun's energy is absorbed by the air directly. Instead, the sun heats the surface, which in turn heats the air above it by direct contact or by the grounding re-radiating at a different wavelength that the air can absorb near to the ground.

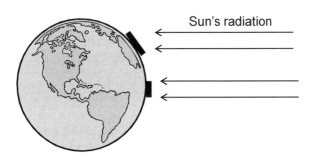

In the tropics the sun is almost overhead. Consequently the surface in the tropics receives more sunshine per square metre than temperate latitudes where the same amount of the sun's energy hits the surface at an angle, and is therefore spread over a greater area.

In addition to receiving different amounts of solar radiation because of latitude, the surface absorbs different amounts of energy depending on its composition. For example water, desert, forest and ice all reflect a different proportion of the heat back into space. The rest of the energy is absorbed, and this may be transferred to the air.

Having absorbed heat, the different surfaces transfer this heat to the air at different rates. In particular, the sea has a great capacity for absorbing heat, so that its temperature does not rise as fast as the land's. The air over land therefore heats up faster than the air over the sea. Because of the land's lower capacity for storage of heat, it also cools down more rapidly than the sea at night. Moreover, the sea only loses its heat slowly during the autumn.

The tilt of the earth's axis also affects the amount of energy received at the surface in the different seasons. In winter in the northern hemisphere, the sun shines at an even more oblique angle and the days are shorter. Less energy is therefore received. The longer nights also allow a longer period of cooling.

Areas of high and low pressure

The differences in the amount of heating of the air caused by latitude and by the type of surface can create small differences in pressure over a wide area (only a few percent) but these are sufficient to cause winds because the air moves in an attempt to equalise the pressures again.

The great intensity of solar heat at the equator causes a belt of warm air which rises, creating a general drop in pressure. Giant convection currents (see diagram below) cause this equatorial air to descend again at about 30° latitude where it creates a region of generally higher pressure, and so less rain. (These areas of persistent high pressure are why most of the world's deserts are not on the equator but in two bands on either side.) Air flows away from these high pressure regions not only back to the equator, but also towards the temperate zones.

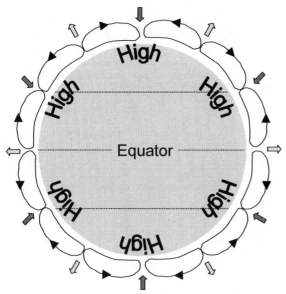

⇨ Rising moist air

⇨ Descending dry air

Another region of high pressure is caused by the air beyond 60° latitude being cold and dense. This polar air meets the tropical air at a boundary called the 'polar front'. In summer the polar front moves nearer the pole. Consequently more of the weather systems that are born along the polar front should pass to the north of the British Isles in summer.

Effect of the earth's rotation
This simple system of flows of hot and cold air from belts of high pressure is complicated by the earth's rotation.

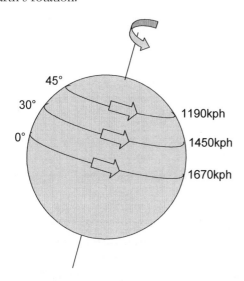

The air at different latitudes has different speeds because of the rotation of the earth. At the equator, the air and the surface are travelling eastwards

together at about 1670kph. At the pole, the rotational speed is zero.

Over the distance from latitude 45° to the pole, on average the change in rotational speed of the earth and atmosphere is about one quarter of a kilometre per hour for each kilometre travelled northwards or southwards.

This difference in speed for each kilometre travelled is far too small to affect the rotation of water going down a plughole, but for weather systems that straddle hundreds and even thousands of kilometres, it has a big effect. The name given to this effect in any rotating system is that of a Frenchman called Coriolis (though he never applied his idea to the theories about the atmosphere).

For example, a mass of air moving from the south towards the North Pole will initially be travelling eastwards more quickly than the local air. Air travelling in the opposite direction from the north towards the equator will be initially travelling eastwards more slowly, ie westwards in relation to the local air.

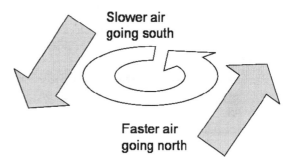

Thus when air flows north and south, the Coriolis Effect tends to set up a rotating system. Although it is not really a force because it is just caused by the momentum of the air, the effect is sometimes called the Coriolis force.

Isobars
Forecasting weather phenomena requires the detailed study of the pressures and temperatures. One of the principal methods is to draw charts, known as a 'synoptic charts' to summarise the variations of pressure at sea level over a large area.

Places with equal pressures are joined by lines called 'isobars', which are analogous to contours on a map. Isobars delineate areas of high pressure and low pressure, much as map contours depict mountains and valleys. In the chart below, the isobars are shown as the thin lines that surround a particularly deep low that will probably pass north of the British Isles. There will be more about the thicker, black frontal lines later in the chapter.

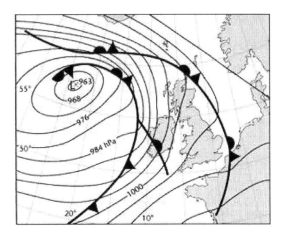

The Coriolis Effect (shown by arrow 1 below) is so strong on the air flowing out of an area of high pressure that it almost equals the force from the pressure difference (arrow 2) drawing it to the low pressure. Consequently the wind does not blow straight from the centre of high pressure area to the centre of the low pressure but almost along the isobars (the unshaded resultant arrow 3). This resultant wind is known as the 'geostrophic wind'. The net effect is that air is deflected around the low pressure anti-clockwise in the Northern Hemisphere.

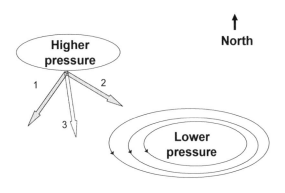

A Dutchman called Buys-Ballot summarised the Coriolis Effect by saying that in the Northern Hemisphere, if you stand with your back to the wind, the lower pressure will always be on your left.

When height-contours on everyday maps are closer together, there is a steeper gradient, and objects will accelerate faster down the slope. The same

principle applies to maps of isobars. When the isobars are closer together, the pressure gradient is greater, and the wind will be stronger.

Wind-gradient and turbulence
The speed of the wind progressively decreases nearer to the surface because of friction with the ground. This reduction in speed is known as the 'wind-gradient'. The decrease in speed depends on the roughness of the surface. Over the sea the wind-gradient is usually less than over the land, because the sea is usually smoother.

The friction arising from obstructions, such as buildings and mountains, produces turbulence and the larger the obstruction, the greater is the turbulence. Typically, gusts from this turbulence can be 60% higher than the mean speed of the wind, although in the middle of cities this can even reach 100%.

Between the blades of grass, the wind-speed will be lowest but clearly a measurement of the wind-speed at this height would not be useful. The surface wind-speed is therefore defined for meteorological purposes as the wind-speed at a height of 10 metres, and this should be measured well away from obstructions that could affect the air-flow.

When the wind changes direction

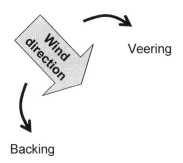

When the wind shifts its direction to a point on the compass that is further clockwise, it is said to 'veer'. If the shift is anti-clockwise, the wind is said to 'back'.

Change in wind direction with height
The friction between the ground and the air reduces the wind's speed, decreasing the momentum that causes the Coriolis Effect. Consequently, the wind near the ground will tend to flow more directly towards the low pressure.

As you descend from about 2000 feet in the Northern Hemisphere, a wind that you experience on your back will tend to take a more direct path by turning left towards the low pressure, as predicted by Buys-Ballot (see diagram below).

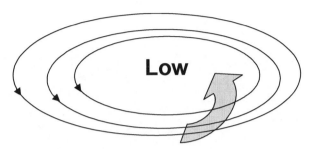

Air near the ground will take a short-cut instead of flowing around the low pressure system

The change with height in speed and direction depends on the strength of the wind and on the roughness of the surface. Typically over land by day the decrease in the wind-speed at the surface compared with 2000 feet will be about 50%, and the wind will back by about 30°. For example, a 20 knot wind from 270° at 2000 feet will often change to about 240° and 10 knots at the surface.

Variation of wind during the day
During the day the slower moving air near the ground is transported upwards by the thermals. In compensation, the air near the ground is replaced by the faster air from higher up. This mixing therefore tends to increase the wind-speed near the surface during the warmest part of the day, when the thermals are strongest. It is known as 'diurnal variation'.

Because the wind brought down from the upper levels has been 'backed' less by friction with the ground, the surface wind will also veer because of this thermal mixing during the day.

At the end of the day, the thermals diminish and so faster air is no longer transported to ground level. The wind-speed therefore often drops in the evening.

Dew point
As well as nitrogen and oxygen, the atmosphere contains substantial amounts of water vapour. Up to 10 grams of water will be in a kilogram of air at 15°C and up to 30 grams at 30°C. (A kilogram of air occupies about 0.81 cubic metres at 15°C.) Though water vapour is lighter than dry air, it can carry more heat. The amount of moisture in the air has therefore a large effect on the amount of heat that can be stored in the air.

Cool air is denser than warm air, because there is less space between the air molecules. This also means that there is less space to fit in water vapour than in warm air. As it cools, air therefore loses its ability to store water. Consequently as moist air rises, it expands (because of the lower pressure) and so its temperature will fall to a value at which its moisture will condense into small droplets. This is known as the 'dew point'. Cloud will form at this temperature.

The dew point may also be reached as air cools down near the ground at night. When this air cools to its dew point, not surprisingly, dew forms, and sometimes fog (see later).

Dry air has a low dew-point, so it needs a very low temperature to squeeze out some droplets.

The percentage of moisture in the air compared with the maximum amount that it could hold for a given temperature is known as the 'relative humidity'.

Lapse-rates
Since warm air is less dense than cold air, a mass of warmer air near the ground will eventually rise like a hot-air balloon, provided the surrounding air is cooler. As the bubble of air rises, it will draw in nearby low lying air. If this nearby air is also warmer, it will follow the initial bubble up in the same column, much to the joy of glider pilots.

Air containing less than the maximum amount of water is known as 'unsaturated air'. Unsaturated air rising from the ground (as in a typical thermal) will lose temperature at about 3°C per thousand feet as it expands. This rate of change is known as the 'dry adiabatic lapse-rate'. ('Adiabatic' is a word that means that the bubble of rising air neither gains nor loses its heat energy to the surrounding air.) The fall in temperature with height is caused by the expansion of the air as the pressure drops, ie the same amount of heat is spread over a larger volume.

The lapse-rate applicable for air of any humidity is always the dry rate, unless the air becomes saturated. As soon as the air cools to the point at which it is saturated, some of its moisture will condense. The condensing water releases the energy that was used to evaporate it. This energy is called 'latent heat'. It is this extra energy that changes the lapse-rate from the dry rate. The energy released is considerable, about 540 calories per gram. In other words the energy released by a gram of condensing water could take 5.4 grams of liquid water from 0°C to boiling. (Freezing only releases 80 calories per gram.)

Consequently, air that is in the process of condensing will have an additional heat source and so only cools at the rate of 1.5°C per thousand feet. (This rate only applies at low levels). This is known as the 'saturated adiabatic lapse-rate'.

If you took measurements of temperature at various heights, you could calculate another lapse-rate. This actual change of the temperature with height is known as the 'environmental lapse-rate'. This measurement would show that the temperature does not always drop steadily with increasing height. In particular, when higher air is warmer than air lower down, an 'inversion' is said to exist. Consequently, the environmental lapse-rate may even be negative in some height bands.

As the air in the thermal cools as it rises, a point will often be reached at which it has the same temperature as the surrounding air, and so that the air stops rising.

If the temperature of the rising air falls to the dew point, clouds will form at this point in the ascent. If there is a large difference between the surface temperature and the dew point, the higher the air can rise higher before it starts forming clouds, ie there will be a high cloud-base.

As a rough rule of thumb (the Bradbury Rule), take the difference between the surface air temperature and the dew point, then multiply by 400 to get the cloud-base in feet. For example, if the surface temperature is forecast to be 23°C and the dew point 10°C, the difference is 13, which puts the cloud-base at about 5200ft (13 x 400). (This assumes that there are no inversions.) If you do not know the dew point, the minimum temperature during the previous night given by the weather forecast is often close enough for this calculation.

A small difference between the surface temperature and dew point implies a low cloud-base or even fog.

Skew T diagrams and similar charts

A source of puzzlement for many is the diagrams used to explain gliding weather forecasts. It is not within the aims of the book to explain how to provide detailed forecasts from these diagrams, but it is appropriate to use them to explain the way in which air might behave at altitude.

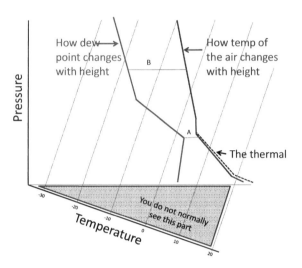

The first thing to point out is that the X-axis is skewed, so that the features of the chart show up more clearly. The part of the chart that is below ground-level is not shown. It might seem odd to those remembering school maths, but axes do not have to be at right-angles to each other.

There are many variations in these diagrams and in their names, depending on the source, but they all plot the change in the air's temperatures versus the change in pressure up through the atmosphere (right-hand line) ie the environmental lapse rate. The left-hand line shows the change in the dew point, ie the temperature at which moisture will condense out of the air. You can read off the air temperature or the dew point from the fine lines coming up from the X-axis.

Other lines are also shown on these diagrams, but these are the main two. Where the two lines get close or even touch is the point at which the air's temperature shown by the right-hand line reaches the dew-point. Clouds form at this point.

The Y-axis is marked in hectopascals (ie millibars). 850hPa is about 5000 feet, 700hPA is about 10,000 feet, 500hPa is at about 18,000 feet and 300hPa is about 30,000 feet which is the where cirrus forms. The pressures are not evenly spaced on the Y-axis because a log scale is used, but don't worry!

Cumulus cloud formation

In the diagram above, another dotted line depicts the change in temperature of a rising mass of air in a thermal. It is has been heated by the ground so that it is hotter than the surrounding air. It will probably be moister, ie have a higher dew-point.

The difference in temperature between the air in the rising thermal and the rest of the nearby air settles down to about 0.5°C, but this is enough to propel it upwards.

If the parcel of air cools to its dew point before it has stopped rising, its moisture will condense, and a cumulus cloud will form usually around the level marked as A on the chart.

On some days when the air is very dry, the cumulus clouds may not form at all, or they may form early in the day, but then gradually fade away as the air becomes warmer. This happens when the "spread" between the two lines at point A is wide (more than 2-4°C), but this effect is often on a knife edge and not easy to predict.

Even though this air has not risen high enough for the temperature to fall to the dew point, the keen-eyed glider pilot may still be able to see where the rising air has begun to condense in haze-caps at the top of otherwise blue thermals.

As water condenses from vapour, its latent heat is released. The air will now cool at 1.5°C per thousand feet, perhaps less than the surrounding air which will help to send the air still higher, and will produce the vertical development of the characteristic cumulus cloud. Moist air is also lighter than dry air, so saturated air rises quickly until all its moisture has condensed. The top of the cumulus is where the air stops rising.

If you attempt a cloud climb, you may experience an increase in the rate of climb caused by these effects as you enter in the cloud. However, your cloud flying abilities and the water droplets on the wing may partly nullify this effect.

Cumulus clouds have a life-cycle. When they are forming, the first few wisps usually betray an already active thermal, and the cloud will grow for a while. Eventually the thermal stops and the cumulus will start to decay. The cloud becomes ragged, and the top of the cloud can sometimes be seen to be curling downwards. From this point in the life-cycle, there will be little lift under the cloud, and often there will be sinking air.

Icing

The small cloud droplets do not freeze when they reach freezing point. Undisturbed, these droplets remain in a 'super-cooled' state often reaching -20°C before freezing and sometimes -40°C. Other particles or larger objects such as gliders are needed to jolt super-cooled water into forming ice. Ice can therefore form on wings from the liquid water in clouds, sometimes very quickly. The aerodynamic properties of the wing are greatly degraded by ice so the stall speed will increase and the efficiency of the wing will be reduced (see later).

Upper level clouds

For a good thermal day, the two lines on the skew chart must not touch. The classic shape is like an angular hour glass. At point B in the skew chart, the lines are well apart and there is no risk here of upper level cloud. However sometimes near the top the two lines will approach indicating high cirrus.

Inversions

When the temperature of the local air does not fall with height but rises or stays constant, a temperature inversion is said to exist.

Inversions can occur for various reasons, but a common cause is a high pressure system. The high pressure has been created by descending air, which heats up because its pressure increases (same amount of heat in a smaller volume). The upper air is therefore warmer than the lower air.

In these conditions, thermals will rise up to the inversion layer and then stop because the surrounding air is at the same temperature, or even higher.

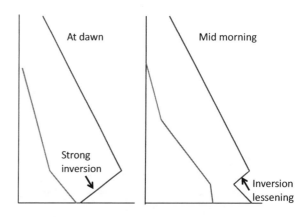

A different type of inversions often occurs in the early morning. The temperature at ground level is near the dew-point (see left-hand diagram above) because it has been cooled by the ground that has been radiating heat overnight. The temperature then stays constant with increasing height. In a skew chart, this means a line sloping up to the right. Later in the morning (right-hand chart), there will still be an inversion but as the sun heats up the ground, the lower part of the right hand line moves to a higher temperature and the inversion will lessen, or even break when the 'trigger' temperature is reached.

In a true inversion, the temperature will increase with height. However, a band in which the temperature does not change with height is often sufficient to stop thermals rising further, though it is not a true inversion. Thermals may take some time to be usable in the morning.

If the thermal's rise has been blocked by an inversion, its air may not have cooled to the dew point, and so no clouds will form. The day is therefore cloudless or 'blue'. A brown layer of trapped dust and pollution usually forms at the inversion level. Visibility may be poor.

The inversion level may be so low that cross-country flying is difficult. Glider pilots then have to grit their teeth when told by non-gliding friends that "It's a lovely day".

On some days when the inversion level is higher and the air is moister, the air rises and some water may condense below the inversion. If air continues to rise, the cloud can reach the inversion and spread out, blocking off the sun for a while. The lack of sun will reduce the number of thermals, though if the air is unstable enough the thermals may continue. The cloud often disperses eventually, but on some days a glider pilot has to contend with an overcast period after a brilliant hour or so. This overcast period can be followed by another cycle of brightness.

If the conditions resist the upward movement of air, the air is said to be 'stable'. Conversely, when conditions allow air to rise easily, the air is said to be 'unstable'.

Precipitation

As more moisture condenses in the same place, the small cloud droplets combine, and are then too heavy to remain airborne. Rain, therefore, falls from the cloud. This occurs when there is no inversion layer stopping the air from rising almost to great heights

However, if the small droplets of moisture continue to rise, the water eventually freezes. The first specks of ice and dust provide points (known as nuclei) around which the super-cooled water in the cloud can freeze. Flakes of snow or even small balls of ice will form around these nuclei, but they will often melt before reaching the ground as rain-showers.

When the up-draught is very strong, the ice particles can be supported for a long period, and so there is more time for the ice to grow. The larger particles do not melt when they descend, and the result is hail.

Fog

The most common type of fog is 'radiation fog'. This forms overnight when the ground loses heat by radiation, and so cools the air near to it. The most likely conditions are when there are no upper clouds and when there are long nights, so that the earth can radiate its heat out into space. A lack of wind will stop higher and warmer warm air mixing with the cold air near the ground. The ground can then cool the nearby air to its dew point, allowing fog to form. Cold air is heavy and so it sinks. Fog therefore first forms in low lying areas such as valleys, but sometimes the conditions allow it to become more widespread.

Coasts also experience a different type of fog, 'advection fog', also called 'sea fog'. In the British Isles, this is formed when moist air has been cooled by passing over a colder sea in winter months. Elsewhere in the world, cold ocean currents can create advection fog in other seasons. Unlike radiation fog, it can form in high winds and can travel long distances.

Air masses

High pressure areas form both in the tropics and in the polar regions and these produce large outflows (air masses) which often arrive over the British Isles.

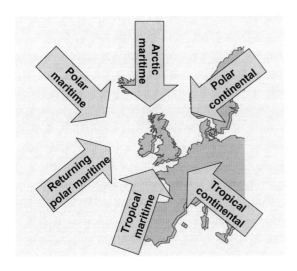

Average wind direction	% of good days
From the S	0%
From the SW	1%
From the W	17%
From the NW	18%
From the N	33%
From the NE	16%
From the E	6%
From the SE	0%
Still air in a high	8%
Total after rounding	**100%**

As you might expect air from the north is colder than air flowing from the south. In addition, warm air that has blown over oceans is moister than warm air that has mainly blown over land.

The air masses that arrive over Britain can be broadly classified as one of six types:

- Tropical maritime – warm and moist
- Tropical continental – warm and dry
- Polar maritime – cold and (fairly) moist
- Polar continental – cold and dry
- Arctic maritime – very cold, so fairly dry
- Returning polar maritime

Returning polar maritime air consists of polar air that has moved southwards over the sea and then turns to the British Isles from the south-west. It is fairly cold but also fairly moist.

The lower levels of these air masses will be cooled or warmed depending on the surfaces they have crossed. This will affect the temperature at each level of the air mass and the probability that thermals will form. A cold air mass allows thermals to form easily because the air that has been heated by the ground can quickly exceed the temperature of the air mass.

When there is a generally warm air mass, a local parcel of air must be heated to a higher temperature before it will rise to form a thermal. Consequently warm air is more stable than cold air.

Tom Bradbury in *Meteorology and Flight* quotes the following percentages for good thermal soaring days in England, but your proximity to coasts and mountains may change these percentages for your area.

Types of cloud

All clouds are formed because moist air has been cooled so that it becomes saturated, often because the air has been forced to rise. In addition to being caused by thermals, clouds can form when warm moist air is undercut by dense, cold air in a front (see *Fronts* later). Upward motion can also occur because of turbulent flow caused by friction with other layers of air or because air is forced over high ground.

These different mechanisms for forming clouds result in several different types of cloud. They are classified using a system devised by Luke Howard that is based on the following Latin words:

- Cirrus – a tuft or filament (e.g. of hair)
- Cumulus – a heap or pile
- Stratus – a layer
- Nimbus – rain bearing
- Alto – from the Latin word for high but it is used to name medium-level cloud.

There are ten basic types of cloud which have been named by combining these words.

High clouds that are found at between 18,000 and 45,000 feet usually consist of ice crystals. There are three sorts:

- Cirrus – white filaments ('mares tails') ('Ci'}
- Cirrocumulus – small rippled elements ('mackerel sky') ('Cc')
- Cirrostratus – transparent sheet, often precedes a warm front ('Cs')

Medium clouds are made of water droplets or water droplets and ice. These are found between 6,500 and 23,000 feet. There are three sorts:

- Altocumulus - layered with rippled/ globular elements, generally white {'Ac}
- Altostratus - thin layer cloud, grey, but sometimes allows weak hazy sunshine ('As')

Weather

- Nimbostratus - thick layer cloud, dark, may produce rain or snow ('Ns')

Most low clouds have bases below 6,500 feet in the British Isles. They are composed of water droplets (though cumulonimbus clouds also include ice crystals). There are four types:

- Stratocumulus – low, lumpy clouds that are often caused when rising air that reaches an inversion layer and spreads out but it is also caused in other ways ('Sc')
- Stratus – grey clouds with a uniform base between 1000 feet and the ground, that often produces rain. ('St')
- Cumulus – individual clouds with varying vertical development, flat base ('Cu').
- Cumulo-nimbus – towering clouds, often with 'anvil tops', sometimes giving thunderstorms or showers of rain or snow. The anvil is caused by ice crystals being blown by fast winds at high altitudes. The flat top is because there is an inversion at the bottom of the stratosphere. ('Cb')

Fronts

The boundary between two different types of air mass is referred to as a 'front'. The most common fronts are those that separate polar maritime and tropical maritime air, and are known as 'polar fronts'.

Fronts are defined according to the air that they bring. When a mass of warm air follows cold air, it is known as a warm front, and if cold air follows warm air, it is a cold front. If a front reverses direction, it changes from being a warm to a cold front (and vice versa).

Fronts are depicted on synoptic charts by thick black lines and shapes that show whether they are warm or cold.

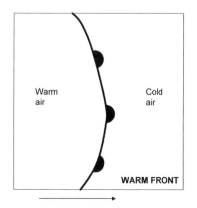

Direction of movement

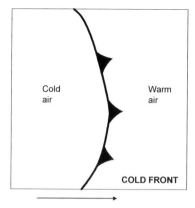

Direction of movement

Further details of warm and cold fronts are given on the next page. It should be noted that the features described for depressions, anticyclones and fronts are only generalised. Every weather system is sufficiently complex to produce many variations on the general theme.

Depressions

An area of low pressure is called a 'depression'. It is usually formed along a polar front by a complex mechanism that involves one of the bands of high-altitude, fast streams of air, known as a jet-stream. What follows is a highly simplistic description of this mechanism.

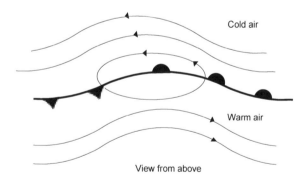

View from above

The first sign of a depression is a bulge of the warm air into side of the cold air. The warm air is rising at this point and the surface pressure is lower as a result. (See diagram above.)

As air flows into this area of low pressure from the colder and higher pressure air, the Coriolis Effect produces a circular flow. The combination of rising air and the circular flow causes the depression to wind itself up and deepen. The whole depression rotates so that cold front moves round towards the warm front. Note in the diagram that there is a warm sector and a larger cold sector.

Weather

Warm front

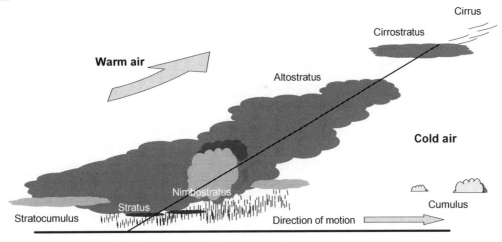

As a warm front moves, the warm moister air, being lighter, is driven above the cold air. As this warm air rises, clouds form at great heights. When the highest cloud reaches the fast moving upper winds, it is smeared out as a band of cirrus in advance of the front. The arrival of a warm front is therefore heralded by this cirrus, then cirrostratus, which reduces and then blocks the sunshine. The wind will veer as the front approaches. The cloud will become thicker and will get very much lower until eventually it starts raining. Note that the slope of the warm front is gentler than is shown in this diagram above, about 1:150. The rain band extends back for about 250 miles. Also note that this is a highly simplified picture of one type of warm front.

Cold front

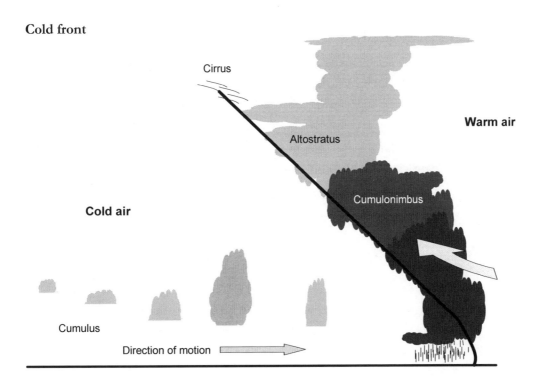

As a cold front moves, the cold air is driven under the warm air. The warm air being moister and lighter can rise rapidly above the colder air. This produces cumulonimbus clouds and heavy showers. The slope of a cold front is less than shown by the diagram, about 1:50 in reality. The rain band extends back by 60-120 miles. This makes a cold front a narrower feature than a warm front, so the rain usually stops sooner. The wind veers and increases as the cold front approaches though at the surface this veering might not occur until a few hours after the front.

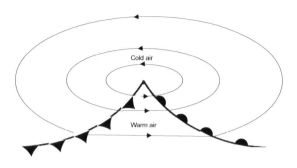

As the air rises and cools in a depression, water vapour condenses to form clouds, and so there is usually rain or snow. Consequently, the weather in a depression is often cloudy, wet and windy.

Because it is an area of low pressure, the Coriolis Effect forces the wind blows in an anticlockwise direction around it. The fronts that produced the depression remain associated with it, while the jet-stream steers the whole system eastwards.

Occluded fronts

The cold front can overtake the warm front, cutting underneath the warm sector and lifting the entire warm air mass. The result is an 'occluded' front. The cross section of a typical occluded front resembles a combination of the warm front and cold front. The result is low cloud and persistent rain.

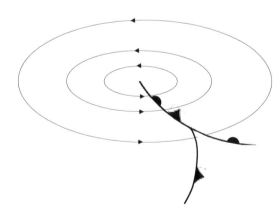

Diagram of an occluded front

Anticyclones

An anticyclone is an area of high pressure, usually caused by descending air. As the winds flow out of it, the Coriolis Effect forces the air to travel clockwise. (The prefix 'anti' in 'anticyclone' is not a good predictor of the wind direction!)

Because clouds are often formed by rising air, the downward movement of the air in an anticyclone often inhibits the formation of cloud, though cloudy highs are annoyingly frequent. The temperature of the descending air rises as its pressure increases (same amount of heat in a smaller volume). Consequently, an inversion is usually produced by an anticyclone. However before the anticyclone fully arrives, there is sometimes a period when air can rise in thermals without it being so unstable that large clouds and showers can form. This is often a good time to fly.

In winter, the light winds and clear skies from an anticyclone can lead to overnight fog or frost. However, in summer an anticyclone in the vicinity of the British Isles often brings fine, warm weather.

Troughs and ridges

Other fluctuations in pressure also occur in addition to the circular depressions and anticyclones. A 'trough' is a belt of low pressure which has characteristics similar to those of a depression. A 'ridge' is a bulge of high pressure producing weather similar to that from an approaching anticyclone. The region between two areas of low pressure systems can be thought as being like a mountain pass between two valleys. Consequently this region of intermediate pressure is known as a 'col'.

Sea-breeze fronts

As the land heats up, air is drawn into thermals. However the sea does not heat up as fast as the land, and cannot create warm air above it. Near coasts this cooler sea air is drawn from above the sea to replace the air drawn into thermals.

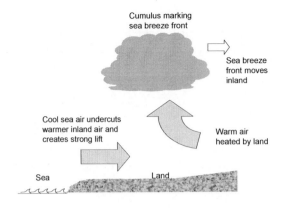

The cold sea-air undercuts the warm air and sends warm air upwards in a front parallel to the coast. The boundary between the cold sea-air and the warm air is sometimes like a mini-cold-front but sometimes it is blue. The front itself often has spectacularly good but narrow lift and you are fortunate if this takes you in a direction that you wanted.

Unfortunately, the air that comes from the sea is moist, and so requires more heating to create thermals. The thermals therefore stop on the seaward side of the front. The front also moves inland so that pilots flying on a good thermic day may therefore find that the soarable area moves further inland during the day.

The sea-breeze front also causes the wind to change speed and direction, sometimes by 180° and by 10 to 20 knots. You may have carefully noted the wind direction during the day, but the change from the passing of a sea-breeze front can come as an unwelcome surprise when you land in a field or even at your home airfield.

The Coriolis Effect may also have swung the wind if the sea-breeze has moved a long way inland, so it may not be blowing straight from the coast.

Like sea-breezes, air masses can also meet elsewhere and create similar 'convergence zones', which can produce spectacular soaring. These can occur in mountainous regions where the lift from two air masses meets above a dividing range.

Note that stable sea-air can also penetrate inland without a sea-breeze front. For example in East Anglia a NE wind is onshore and produces poor soaring conditions.

A similar effect to the arrival of sea-air can occur when there is fog over some places and bright sunshine over other places. The thermals draw in air from the colder place so that the sunny area is suddenly flooded with fog which shuts off the thermals.

Thunderstorms

Most thunderstorms are associated with towering cumulonimbus clouds. Three conditions are needed: an unstable air mass, moist air at ground level and a source of upward movement, often because of heating, but flow up mountain slopes and fronts also cause air to rise strongly.

As the air rises, the condensation of the moisture starts as usual at a cloud-base of a few thousand feet. The moist air is light, the air mass is unstable and so the moist air rises further. The latent heat that is released by condensation stops the air from cooling as fast as the surrounding air and so it allows the air to continue to rise. The air will rise to great heights if there is no inversion strong enough to prevent it. When the moisture freezes, the latent heat of freezing releases more energy and so causes the air to rise even further. The rising air can even reach the stratosphere where an inversion stops it. The strong winds at that height blow the top of the cumulo-nimbus cloud downwind, giving it an anvil shape.

Not all cumulonimbus clouds are thundery. They are often present in cold fronts. Some just produce heavy showers or hail. However, thundery CuNims have particularly strong up-draughts and down-draughts that bring ice and water in contact, though flowing in opposite directions. The process is not fully understood, but it seems that the friction between the up-draughts and the down-draughts containing water and ice produces a static charge. Since the two flows are going in opposite directions, the charges are separated and are unable to neutralise each other. Eventually the charges become so great that they will neutralise by a lightning bolt, usually to the opposite charges in other clouds but sometimes they will earth by a ground-strike.

Thunderstorms go through three stages: cumulus, mature and dissipating. In the cumulus stage the clouds build up to impressive heights (cumulus congestus) but they are otherwise apparently benign sources of strong up-draughts.

In the mature stage, the cloud contains both strong up-draughts and down-draughts. The down-draughts can be severe. (Powerful down-draughts in the USA have downed airliners on approach and are known as 'micro-bursts'.) However even British thunderstorms produce sudden downward gusts. The wind changes direction as these down-draughts fan out well ahead of the storm. In addition to the strong gusty winds, heavy rain or hail can be expected.

Risks from thunderstorms

Since flying in wave has become better understood, few glider pilots have deliberately flown in thunderstorms and with good reason, though many have found themselves near them by accident. Even professional pilots in airliners try to avoid thunderstorms, so it is even more hazardous for glider pilots.

The risks of flying in thunderstorms are:
- Severe shocks to the pilot
- Strong up-draughts that could take you above the heights at which you need oxygen
- Down-draughts that can fling you towards the ground
- Sudden changes in the wind strength and direction
- Rain and hail reducing visibility
- Icing
- Turbulence
- Nil visibility in the cloud (leading to a risk of loss of control and over-speeding)
- Baling out and the parachute then going upwards.

The controls of the glider should have been electrically connected ('bonded') by the manufacturer to reduce the differences in potential that may otherwise pass through the pilot. Bonding also stops the control rods being welded together by the arc.

If a glider has been hit by lightning, do not assume the bonding has worked. The damage may not be visible from outside. The glider must be thoroughly inspected before it flies again.

A winch-launch can provide a classic demonstration of a lightning conductor, even before thunder and lightning have started elsewhere. Even if there has been no local lightning, the charge may already be building up. A wire flown into the vicinity will earth the charge. This can happen long before the charge is strong enough to jump through air.

Stop launching if lightning is seen or thunder is heard, or if a CuNim is sighted within ten miles of the site. Crackling on the radio will also indicate that storms are present. Note that in some conditions the CuNim may be partly hidden by overcast clouds and may be closer than it seems.

On the ground the thunderstorm will usually generate squalls, causing great changes in the speed and direction of the wind. Landing a glider in these conditions is hazardous.

Once you have landed, your risks are not over. Firstly, the glider can be blown over by the gusty winds. Moreover, between 30 and 60 people are struck by lightning each year in the UK, though only three or four of these die. Airfields are particularly exposed places, so the risks for glider pilots are real. Metal vehicles are safe shelter but trees, golfing umbrellas, caravans, gliders and other non-metallic shelter should not be used as shelter.

If you are caught in the open and you feel your skin tingle or your hair rise, you are about to be struck. Crouch low on the ground and put your hands on your head and your elbows on your knees so the lightning is less likely to pass through your chest, and so stop your heart. Do not touch the ground with your hands.

If you find someone who has been hit by lightning, the heart and breathing may have stopped completely, but these can be restarted by the usual mouth-to-mouth and cardiac compression techniques. You should try resuscitation for 20 to 30 minutes.

Active fronts and squalls

As a warm front arrives, the cloud base will lower, the wind will usually increase progressively, and it will start raining gradually. However, an approaching cold front or a trough can be more dramatic. The bad weather can arrive at surprising speed and can include squalls and sometimes thunderstorms.

From a day with relatively quiet winds, very strong winds can develop within a minute as a squall line approaches. The squall will contain heavy rain, or possibly hail or even snow. There is often strong lift in front of the approaching front but the conditions behind should cause the prudent pilot to land immediately.

If a squall is imminent, put the gliders away, but if this has not been possible, park the gliders securely with the pilots strapped in the gliders, with air-brakes open and with tyres to prevent the gliders from moving. People may even have to hold down the wing-tips of the gliders as the squall passes.

Wind strength and safe gliding

You should already be aware of wind-gradient in even moderate winds and the effect that it should have on your planned approach speed. However as the wind gets even stronger other effects should be appreciated.

When the wind's speed in its gusts approaches the stalling speed of the glider, flying becomes dangerous. The average speed of the wind may be acceptable, but it is the gusts that cause the problems.

Remember that the wind strength will increase during the day because of thermal mixing. A strong wind in the morning may gradually become dangerous later in the day before anyone notices.

Even if you can land the glider in a strong wind, it may be difficult to keep it on the ground. In these conditions, it is imperative that the pilot remains strapped in the glider and keeps the airbrakes open. Do not park gliders in the open in very blustery conditions, and ensure than canopies are locked shut to prevent them blowing open or closed.

On calm days it does not matter with which wing you walk when moving a glider. However on a windy day the choice of wing matters greatly. On the upwind wing-tip you can use your weight to hold down the wing. On the downwind side, you cannot easily prevent your wing dropping to the ground. The upwind wing may then continue upwards and lift the glider off the ground.

The standard wind-sock used at gliding clubs will point straight back at 20kt.

Wind and mountains

When a wind meets a slope, the air must rise, if it cannot spill around the sides of the hill. A smooth hill does not interrupt the flow and gives the best lift. In contrast, steep cliffs can be turbulent very close to the face, even with some downward air towards the base. The trees on wooded hills can also produce turbulence and these hills can also be unreliable low down.

Downwind of the crest of the hill, the air will descend again and is turbulent. This is known as 'curl over'. The rate of sink here can be impressive.

When the air rises up a slope, the moisture that it contains can condense, forming 'orographic' cloud and rain. After losing its moisture, the air will have been heated slightly by the condensation. On the downwind side of large mountains the air-flow is therefore warmer and drier and is known as a 'föhn wind'. A gap in the clouds that is caused downwind of a mountain is sometimes known as a "föhn gap".

Large mountains not only produce an up-draught, they can also funnel the winds into a new direction and increase its speed. The role of the Rhone Valley and the Alps in creating the Mistral is a good example, but there are many other instances elsewhere.

In the mountainous areas, the wind strength and direction can change dramatically with height and with place. For example, Gap airfield in southern France sometimes launches on its southerly runway on windy days when airfields just beyond nearby mountains are using their northerly runways.

Downwind of the mountains you may encounter rotor (see later). In extreme cases rotor has damaged gliders in flight, but this is rare. Nevertheless some caution is needed. In rotor you should fly at less than the maximum manoeuvring speed because full control deflections are likely. If you are landing at some mountain airfields in strong winds eg Aspres-sur-Buëch in southern France, the rotor can reach the ground, making landing impossible in some wind directions.

Even if there is no rotor, the pilot flying downwind of a mountain can experience some powerful sink in the curl-over. At the sites on top of hills such as the Long Mynd, your approach is through this down-draught, so you must be much higher and closer in on your final turn than at a 'flat-land' site. Flights with an experienced local instructor are therefore recommended, if you are new to flying in windy conditions in mountains.

Effects of mountains on thermals

If a slope is angled to face the sun, the surface will be quickly heated and in turn this will heat the air along the length of the slope. At the top of the mountain the surrounding air will be cold. The heated air at the top of the slope will therefore rise quickly in a thermal, pulling up more air to be warmed by the slope. The up-slope wind that is created is called an 'anabatic wind' and it pulls in air from the valley towards the mountain creating a valley wind. Consequently the lift near the slope is a combination of ridge lift and thermal lift, sometimes called 'thermodynamic lift'. The mountain thermals often continue above the peaks and are powerful enough to break through an inversion layer that might be blocking the rise of thermals in the valley.

Because mountains have a greater ability to produce thermals, cumulus clouds therefore tend to form early in the day over higher ground. However this also means mountainous areas are more likely to trigger thunderstorms than nearby flat areas.

The literal downside of thermodynamic lift is that is there also strong sink into the valley on the downwind side of the mountain. Since valleys tend to be linear features, this sink can continue for long distances. Pilots in mountainous areas must therefore fly with considerable margins of safety.

From the middle of the day until the thermals subside in the evenings, the air in the valleys is drawn towards the mountains by the strong thermals. The opposite effect then occurs at night and in the early morning. The mountainous areas are efficient radiators of heat, creating cold air. This cold air flows down the slopes producing 'katabatic' winds. When the mountain slopes heat up again the next day, the flow reverses once more.

Waves
Often when the wind blows over a hill, it merely goes up and down and creates a few eddies. However when the conditions are just right, strong, standing waves appear. The ideal conditions are:

- Hill aligned within 30° of perpendicular to the wind at 10,000 feet
- Wind direction roughly constant to at least 18,000 feet
- Wind speed which does not decrease with height
- A slight anticyclonic curve to the isobars which indicates one or more stable layers to "put the lid" on showers

The stable layers of air are constrained by the air above and below them, so they are able to oscillate like a spring. The 'twang' is usually provided by a mountain, or even just a small hill. The vibration can continue for many wavelengths downwind, with wavelengths of typically one to three miles. As a stable layer vibrates, the air above it is also forced to move up and down so the lift can go to great heights, far higher than the originating mountain.

Sometimes fortuitously spaced mountains downwind of the first mountain can reinforce a wave by adding an additional 'twang'. Occasionally thermals will also add or subtract from the wave. This can produce some puzzling effects when flying cross-country in thermals. From a patch of excellent thermals, the pilot encounters poor thermals until he flies on to the next area where the both the wave and the thermals are going up.

As the air steeply descends from the primary wave, some of it usually flows upwind, producing a region of turbulence called 'rotor'. The glider pilot who is searching for wave low down may find the rotor and may experience a rough ride until the glider climbs out. In moist air the rotor is often marked by an innocuous-looking cloud, but on closer examination this cloud can sometimes be seen to be a horizontally rolling vortex.

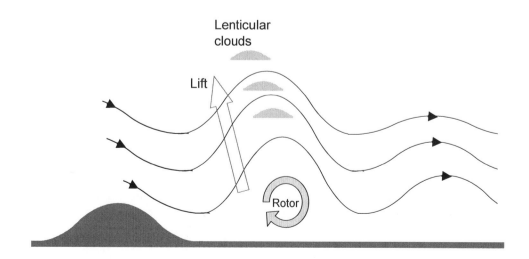

Where the air is going up in a wave, its moisture can condense to form very smooth lens-shaped ('lenticular') clouds. As the air descends in the down wave, the moisture evaporates. These clouds therefore appear stationary, but actually are being continuously created and destroyed. Because these clouds are not moving, they can appear to be higher than they really are. In Scotland lenticular clouds can be seen as low as 4000 feet.

Cross-winds

Dealing with cross-winds should be within the abilities of any cross-country pilot. However the risks from cross-winds should not be ignored.

Check your flight manual for the maximum proven cross-wind component for a safe landing and take-off.

A cross-wind can cause a glider to drop a wing on take-off. If the tip catches on the ground, the glider may cartwheel and seriously injure the occupants. Always pull off the launch if the wing hits the ground on the ground run on a winch-launch. (For this reason you should have your left hand on the release knob.) On smooth short grass or concrete, it is often possible to recover from a dropped wing on an aerotow, but there are no guarantees here either.

Landing in cross-winds also has risks because of turbulence from trees and buildings at the side of the field. The vortex from a large hangar can create an unexpected gust which could surprise an unwary pilot. The glider may also swing into a cross-wind shortly after it has landed and ground-loop in the process.

Temperature and gliders

The lapse-rate usually predicts that it will be much colder at altitude and you should dress accordingly, but the low temperature also affects the glider itself. A high-flying glider will be very cold. If a cold glider flies into cloud, or more rarely, if rain falls on a cold glider, the moisture will instantly freeze. For example, if you are flying in wave near a lenticular cloud, stay away from the cloud because the cloud will instantly freeze on your cold canopy, greatly reducing your visibility. For similar reasons when descending from great heights, fly into the gaps in the cloud rather than through them.

The ice can also affect performance and the controls. The wings will become less efficient and

more likely to stall. The suggested remedy for the main controls is to use them constantly, especially during a descent through cloud. However opening and closing the airbrakes may let in water into the boxes making it more likely they will freeze shut.

The control linkages will also expand and contract with the temperature and the lubrication in the control joints may also be affected. The net result is that the controls may feel stiff on days with very low temperatures.

The pitot tubes and static vents may also become blocked with ice making the instruments inoperative. In extreme cases, ice may affect the total weight distribution of the glider and may even degrade radio signals.

Perspex® canopies become very brittle in cold conditions. The slightest amount of stress, such as closing the canopy on a seat strap, can crack it.

Fog

The official definition of fog is visibility less than one kilometre, though most people recognise it when they see it.

Launching when fog is present is risky because of the prospect of not only flying in cloud but also of landing with no visibility.

Very often you can look directly upwards from the ground and see blue sky, but when looking to the side, the visibility is poor. In the air this means that you can only see a small area of the ground below you, if any at all. Finding the airfield in these conditions can be impossible.

Rain

Rain not only affects visibility, but also the performance of the glider. It is therefore better to land in advance than to try to fly through a large area of heavy rain. This situation should be distinguished from the days with good thermals, when you may be rained on for a short period by one cloud and yet you are still be able to reach another area of lift.

In very heavy rain, you may have to open the clear vision panel to get any sort of view of where you are going. You may also find that the vents for ASI and the vario have become blocked by water and that the instruments are no longer reading sensibly.

Weather

Some gliders are noticeably affected by rain on the wings and their performance deteriorates because the air-flow over the wings and tail-plane becomes turbulent sooner. The performance of wooden gliders is less affected by rain than glass gliders, though these vary greatly. Some glass gliders such as the PIK20 produce a noticeable judder when wet.

Do not launch if there is rain-water, snow or frost on the glider because this will affect the stalling speed. Dry off the whole glider first. Having dry wings is especially important if the air temperature is close to freezing.

Snow

Snow has a much greater effect on visibility than even heavy rain. It is difficult to see anything other than snow as it appears a few metres in front of the glider. The prop-wash from an aerotow after snow has fallen can also create a blizzard.

Snow also does not blow off flying surfaces as well as water droplets, so the glider's performance is degraded even more.

On completely smooth snow, recognising the airfield will be more difficult as the familiar features are obscured. The perception of height may also be affected, so that landings are more difficult to judge.

Hail

Hail is generated in a heavy, squally shower or a thunderstorm. Visibility is likely to be greatly reduced, possibly to nil, and the wind is likely to be exceptionally gusty. There is an additional risk in places that have more violent thunderstorms than the UK. In these places, exceptionally large hailstones can damage the surface of gliders and even cars.

Weather forecasts

The law requires the commander of the aircraft immediately before flight to "examine the current reports and forecasts of the weather conditions on the proposed flight path, being reports and forecasts which it is reasonably practicable for him to obtain, in order to determine whether Instrument Meteorological Conditions prevail or are likely to prevail during any part of the flight." For gliding IMC are certain if the pilot intends to get within 1,000 feet of a cloud-base over 3,000 feet. Nevertheless it is always good idea to know what the weather will be doing during the day:

- Will the wind's speed or direction change?
- What is the expected cloud-base?
- How much cloud cover?
- Is a front anticipated?
- How long will soaring conditions last?
- Are showers possible?
- Will there be a sea-breeze?
- Is wave forecast?
- What will be the visibility?

The Internet provides a rich source of weather forecasts and other information about meteorology.

The best list of sources of tutorials for glider pilots is at: http://www.weatherjackwx.co.uk/

Weatherjack's site also provides a wide variety of links to many other useful web sites, including:
- UK Meteorological Office
- Satellite pictures
- Soundings and tutorial
- Web-cams
- Plain language forecasts
- METARS (met reports from airfields) and TAFs (forecasts from airfields)

An excellent free service which repays a little study is RASP. The two versions are on:
http://rasp.stratus.org.uk/
http://rasp.inn.leedsmet.ac.uk/RASPtable.html
The Stratus version has a useful tutorial on skew T diagrams and the convective boundary layer.

Met Office

The Met Office's web site has many useful pages of information about meteorology. You can register for a useful free general aviation briefing, including five-day synoptic charts, Form 214, rainfall radar, satellite pictures and TAFs. There is also a downloadable booklet explaining some of the data. http://www.metoffice.gov.uk/aviation/ga

Form 214

One of the Met Office's free charts is known as Form 214. This provides the forecast wind strength and direction and temperature for a range of times at various heights (see below). A related free chart is Form 215 for below 10000 feet.

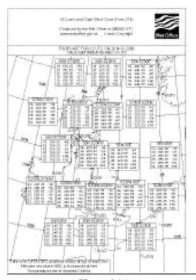

Form 214

To take one of the boxes on Form 214 (Bristol):

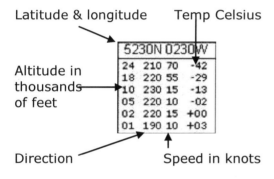

Latitude & longitude   Temp Celsius

Altitude in thousands of feet

Direction   Speed in knots

TAFs

Also available free from the Met Office are Terminal Aerodrome Forecasts which are issued for individual airfields. The duration of these forecasts is usually for a 9 hours but can be longer. These should not be confused with METARs which are reports of current conditions at an airfield. The format is confusing for the uninitiated.

[Station ID] [Origin Date/Time] [Valid Period] [Wind] [Horizontal Visibility] [Significant weather] [Cloud cover] [Significant changes]

EGUB 051344Z 0515/0523 29020G35KT 9999 SCT045 BECMG 0515/0518 29015G25KT

In this example of a TAF for RAF Benson, the airfield is EGUB and it was issued on 05 Jan at 13:44 Zulu (which is GMT). It applied on 5 Jan from 15:00 until 23:00. The wind was forecast to be from 290 degrees at 20 knots gusting to 35 knots. (For the wind direction you may occasionally see VRB meaning variable.) 00 means calm conditions. The visibility is measured in metres. The maximum

visibility is 9999 which is 10km. SCT scattered cloud at 4,500 feet. BECMG = Becoming less windy during the forecast period between 15:00 and 18:00.

Cloud cover is described as follows:

FEW	Few	1-2 eighths (octas or oktas)
SCT	Scattered	3-4 eighths
BKN	Broken	5-7 eighths
OVC	Overcast	8 eighths
NSC	No significant cloud below 5,000 feet	

A full list of the abbreviations is on the Met Office web-site, but note that TSRA means thunderstorms with rain.

Volmet

The following radio frequencies give continuously updated meteorological reports

- South   128.6 MHz
- North   126.6 MHz
- Main   135.375 MHz
- Scottish   125.725 MHz

Each station gives the weather that has been reported by 9 airports. London Main gives the three London airports and European reports.

The terminology that they use is mainly self-explanatory. CAV-OK means that the Ceiling and Visibility are OK ie more than 10km visibility, no cloud below 5000 feet and no other weather.

Summary

The following points should be understood:

- Conditions where the weather is marginal, rarely produce good flying, so do not risk it
- Get a check flight if you are flying in unfamiliar conditions, especially in mountains
- Strong winds require careful ground handling as well as prudent flying
- Be careful of the change in wind-speed and direction from sea-breeze fronts when you are landing
- Avoid thunderstorms

Questions

1. What does 'Buys-Ballots' Law state for the northern hemisphere?
2. If a due westerly wind is forecast to veer by 10°, from what direction will it then come?

3. How does the wind direction vary as you descend from 2000 feet?

4. There is a strong cross-wind. You want to land alongside of and downwind of a row of trees and large hangar, what might happen?

5. What causes the wind-speed to increase in the morning and decrease in the evening?

6. What will the effect of a sea-breeze front have on your plans if you have to fly across one?

7. What effect will the passage of a sea-breeze front have had, if you make a field landing?

8. What is the dew point?

9. What are the environmental lapse-rate, the dry adiabatic lapse-rate and the saturated lapse-rate?

10. The maximum temperature is forecast to be 22 °C and the dew point is 7 °C. Roughly how high will cloud-base be?

11. You are ridge soaring and find that cloud is forming over the hill. What is the type of cloud called?

12. In the summer, what is often the first sign of an approaching warm front?

13. You are landing your glider near a thunderstorm, what is your greatest risk?

14. What is the cause of radiation fog?

15. What would be the effect on thermals of an inversion layer in an anticyclone in the summer?

16. You notice that the cumulus clouds are rising to great heights above their bases and flattening at the tops. What could happen next?

17. It is July and the weather feels fresh. A ridge of high pressure is forecast. What weather would you expect?

18. There has been a shower while your glider has been at the front of the launch queue but flying is about to restart. What should you do?

19. You are on a gliding holiday in the Pyrenees and because thunderstorms are forecast, you decide not to fly that day. Should you de-rig the glider? What might you experience near a rotor cloud?

20. In which direction would the wind tend to blow in the mountains in high summer during the afternoon?

USE AND CARE OF PARACHUTES

Introduction
This chapter begins with a discussion of the main issue in the use of parachutes, namely the decision to jump. The other sections provide some additional information about the use and care of parachutes.

The decision
Before you fly you should always consider the circumstances under which you may need to use a parachute. Consider it as one of the eventualities in your pre-flight checks. For instance, what you would do if you have a collision? Are you going to jump?

Jumping out of a glider might seem dramatic, excessive, expensive and scary, but these are minor considerations compared with the higher risks of staying with a damaged glider. Before you decide on your probable action, think about the following true stories.

A carrier pilot successfully ejected after an engine failure immediately after launch. The chances of reacting in time in these situations are low. He was asked when he made the decision to eject. His reply was "Ten years earlier".

An experienced competition pilot collided with another competitor at about 3000 feet. He was seen checking the controls to ensure the glider was still flyable. He descended to 1000 feet at which height the tail fell off and he was unable to bale out.

The g-forces in a damaged glider could quickly increase as its speed builds up. These forces may quickly exceed your strength, making an exit impossible. (Just imagine getting out of a bath-tub at 2g even without an instrument panel and without a parachute on your back.) If you are going to get out at all, an early decision may be essential.

Many pilots who have made a jump have said that the decision was obvious. Sadly, we cannot ask how the decision was made by some of the pilots who did not jump.

You should therefore decide before you next fly the circumstances in which you would jump. You should also rehearse how you would get out of each glider that you fly. Work out if you have to pull both the canopy-release and the canopy-jettison knobs.

Why might you jump?
After collisions, the most likely other reasons for jumping are rigging mistakes or structural failures, but both are uncommon. A rigging mistake usually manifests itself shortly after take-off, but not necessarily. It is also hard to damage a well-maintained glider below 75 or 80 knots unless you do a tail-slide (but please do not take this as a challenge). However above the maximum manoeuvring speed, it is possible to damage the glider by applying large control deflections or by over-speeding, such as when emerging from a cloud out of control.

Other causes of jumps are varied and are even rarer. For example, a massive lightning strike blew apart a glass two-seater; the canopy blew off a two-seater after poor aerobatics and hit the fin; one pilot heard an unexpected clunk and so baled out of a probably serviceable glider; and another pilot failed to do up his seat straps and was ejected by turbulence through the canopy whilst on aerotow. However these are all isolated examples and may never recur. This primary cause of baling out is therefore collision.

The rate of jumping seems to be less than one every year on average in the UK, which is spread over a pilot population of about 8,000. However, if you are planning to fly for another twenty years, the odds of it happening to you begin to look more significant, especially if your look-out is poor.

Sensible precautions
Some of the following points may seem obvious, but are worth re-stating nevertheless.
- Always wear a parachute even for routine flights. (This is a BGA recommendation if the glider is built to accept parachutes)
- The parachute harness should be tightened so that it is snug when standing up. (A loose harness could cause injury.) Some parachutes also have straps at waist level that should also be tightened to get a good fit.

Use and care of parachutes

- Protect your parachute from damp, spillages, ultra-violet (sun) and extremes of heat and cold. A parachute stored in a trailer over winter may reach -20°C in Scotland and left in a cockpit in the midday sun could reach 40°C.

- Keep parachutes in its bag in a warm, dry place when not in use to prevent the line stows (like thick rubber bands) from perishing. Do not keep the parachutes in the glider or trailer

- Inspect your parachute for stains, bent pins, fraying seams, worn Velcro, ineffective stowage of the rip-cord handle. Look at the metal knob at the end of the rip-cord that stops the handle falling off. They have been known to fail

- If any part of the canopy or any rigging lines are showing, assume it is unserviceable

- The life expectancy and the repacking frequency of emergency parachutes are unregulated in the UK. Different manufacturers suggest different lifetimes and repack intervals. Most recommend a repack interval of six months, so do not delay re-packing.

Parachute handling
Dangling a parachute by its harness puts unnecessary strain on the stitching. Sport parachutists handle parachutes like babies. Most of the time, it should be carried in its bag.

If you put your left arm through the harness first, you are less likely to pull the rip-cord accidentally as you reach round for the other strap.

Rehearsing
If you are flying in a two-seater, before you take off, discuss the bale-out procedure and how the order to jump will be given. The words 'Bale-out' said three times are generally suggested, though the reality may be different. If flying solo or dual, mentally rehearse which knobs you would pull and which straps you would undo before you take off. You will require less time, if the need to jump arises, if you have thought about your actions in advance.

Habitually undoing your parachute harness before you leave the glider after a routine flight, is said by some to increase the chances of that you will undo the parachute harness in an emergency.

Jumping
Do not worry about what will happen to the glider. You do not need to steer it away from habitation before your exit. Even in towns, the vast majority of the area is unoccupied by people.

Jettison the glider's canopy first. If you undo your seat straps first, you can be thrown against the canopy, and then be unable to reach the jettison knob. If you then cannot jettison the glider's canopy, at least you would still be strapped in for the impact. The canopy may be held in place by air pressure, so you may have to push it away.

Stand up and jump out, pulling the rip-cord as soon as you are clear. You may need some effort to pull the rip-cord, but you can use two hands. Pull in the direction of the ripcord housing, ie. if the housing routes over the left shoulder, pull downwards towards the left foot. Acceleration in freefall is 32 feet per second per second with a terminal velocity of 120 mph reached in 12 seconds. At this speed an asymmetric body position will result in violent rotation which may seriously compromise the deployment of the parachute. The drilled procedure of "look, reach, pull" will ensure adequate clearance from the aircraft and a reasonably slow freefall velocity.

If you cannot stand up vertically, because the glider is not horizontal, you may have to kick to push clear.

The parachute canopy will open with a jolt. If you are above 500 feet by the time you pull the rip-cord, you should land relatively safely. However emergency parachutes are designed to be life-savers rather than limb-savers.

At great altitude it is always better to open the parachute immediately than to try free-falling. It is likely that you will to lose control when free-falling, and so not to be correctly oriented when you have to pull the rip-cord. A long descent under your parachute may be cold but should not be fatal.

Steering a parachute
An emergency parachute is circular in shape after it is fully open but there are mesh-covered drive vents located at the rear of the canopy that remove this symmetry. These drive vents make the canopy steer-able and create an air speed of about 5kph (depending upon body weight and altitude) in the direction you are facing.

A steerable canopy also has an air-speed of about 5 knots. This allows the pilot a degree of control and the means to avoid landing hazards – roads, buildings, power lines, water, etc. The parachute has four risers (these are the straps that attach the harness to the canopy). You turn to the right by pulling down the right rear riser by 15cm to 30cm (similarly for a left turn). The parachute will continue turning until you stop pulling. It takes about 8 - 10 seconds to complete a full 360 degree turn. Great precision in your first attempt is unlikely but at least try to land into wind.

Landing with a parachute

Landing has been compared to jumping from a first-floor window. However this does not convey the lateral speed that you may also have because of the wind. Think of the window being in the upper deck of a moving double-decker bus. The horizontal speed will add to the shock of landing.

The ground will seem a long way away for a long time. In the last few seconds of the descent, it will appear to rush up at you (ground rush). It is easy to change from a good landing position at this moment as the reaction will be to fend off the ground with an arm or leg. That is when injuries occur... Good discipline is important, so hold the landing position!

Keep your feet and knees together and bend your knees. Put your chin on your chest, clench your teeth, hunch your shoulders and hold the webbing high up. Keep your elbows in. The trick is not to face fully forward or backwards to your direction of travel but to land side-on, immediately crumpling and rolling onto your thighs, buttocks then your shoulder. This dissipates the energy. If you try to stay upright, you increase the chances of injury.

Quickly get up, run round the canopy to the downwind side and pull in the lines to deflate it. Otherwise you could be dragged along the ground.

If landing in trees, you should raise your feet slightly before you arrive and yours legs together. You should also shield your eyes from the foliage by crossing your arms in front of your face. If suspended, wait for help before trying to climb down.

If suspended from power wires, avoid touching anything at all and let no-one approach you until the power is confirmed as off. The information will only be given reliably by an electricity company operative.

At all costs, try to avoid landing in water.

Summary

The main points are:

- Have you decided on what you would do after any collision?
- Mentally rehearse baling out
- Look after your parachute
- Land with your feet and knees together.

Questions

1. In addition to thinking about launch failures, what else should you include in the eventualities part of your pre-flight checks?
2. You collide with another glider but your own glider seems OK. What should you do?
3. You are descending on a parachute. The ground is rushing up fast, what should be your body position?

YOUR SILVER DISTANCE FLIGHT

Introduction

The secret of success is to have as much prepared in advance as possible. Know your glider and how its equipment works, and plan the probable routes. This chapter describes this process in more detail and gives a few hints about the flight itself.

The glider and its equipment

You must be current on the glider that you will be flying. You should have read its flight manual and had many local flights in it already so that you know you can land it reliably in a small field. You should know how the instruments work. Your first cross-country flight is not the time to learn about how a GPS or an unfamiliar variometer works. You also should know how to rig and to de-rig the glider.

Check the wheel-brake of the glider. (If there is no front skid, stopping in a short field could be a big problem without a wheel-brake.)

What to take – In flight

A check-list of things to take can help you concentrate on getting ready to fly. Of the following items the starred items are essential:

- ❖ An up-to-date half-million-scale aeronautical chart, marked with your route (mandatory)
- ❖ Water to drink during the flight (half a litre an hour) plus water for after landing so take 2 litres even for a Silver distance
- ❖ Charged batteries for the glider
- ❖ Adequate clothing for the flight, especially for your feet if it is not high summer
- ❖ Sun-hat and protection from the sun for your arms. Do not fly with a large brim or a peak on your cap. It will obstruct your look-out
- ❖ Sun-glasses (and sun-cream if you burn)
- ❖ Flight recorder to record the flight
- ❖ Any medication you may be taking
- ❖ A spare pair of glasses may be needed to comply with your medical certificate
- ❖ Urination arrangements
- • A wrist-watch
- • In-flight snacks

What to take – For after the flight

- ❖ Mobile phone and contact numbers
- ❖ Additional clothing for after landing, including something warm and waterproof
- ❖ Money and credit cards for petrol and possibly to buy dinner for the retrieve crew
- ❖ Badge claim form
- ❖ A cheque book to pay for an aerotow retrieve at another club or to make a donation to a farmer's favourite charity
- ❖ Insurance certificate (by law)
- ❖ Airworthiness Review Certificate (by law)
- • Tissues or toilet paper
- • Reading material for while you are waiting to be retrieved
- • Canopy lock, so you can leave the glider without the risk of losing possessions
- • Tie down kit to stop the glider blowing over if you have to leave it
- • Small torch with fresh batteries, in case the retrieve is delayed until after dark
- • Pen and paper for recording information and leaving messages
- • Band-Aid for small cuts from barbed wire and thorns.

European Law will soon require you to fly with your licence, a valid medical certificate and personal identification document containing his/her photo.

Your car and the trailer

Check that your car is roadworthy. The tyres should be inflated and the car should also have coolant water, brake fluid, oil and fuel. The screen-wash bottle must also be full. Ensure that your insurance cover will allow any of the drivers that might retrieve you to drive your car.

Do not take your spare car keys, if you are expecting a retrieve using your own car! Leave the keys where your retrieve crew can find them.

Check that the trailer is roadworthy. In particular inspect the tyres. The tyres wear out even if the tread has done little mileage. Look at the sidewalls for cracking and replace the tyres if in doubt. Check the tyre pressures, including the trailer's spare. Ensure all rigging aids are in the trailer and there is not a glider in the trailer already.

Requirements for a Silver Distance flight

The first cross-country flight is usually made to get the distance element of the Silver Badge. This requires a flight of over 50 kilometres. This can be done as a free distance ie just land somewhere more than 50 kilometres from where you took off.

If you do it as a closed circuit task, the length of the longest leg must exceed 50 kilometres. 25 kilometres out and 25 back would not count. If you do an out-and-return, it is prudent to declare the first leg as your Silver Distance. You should also consult the Sporting Code (see BGA web-site) for the requirements for flight recorders. The use of cameras for turn-points has been phased out http://www.fai.org/gliding/taxonomy/term/16

To count as part of the Silver Badge, the flight must be observed by witnesses (not necessarily Official Observers) at launch and landing. An OO is only needed later to scrutinise the evidence.

If you land more than 50 kilometres away to get your Silver Distance, you will need to find an official observer or two witnesses to certify your place of landing. Take the badge claim form with you for local witnesses in case only one person comes to retrieve you.

The 1% rule

If you are flying a Silver Distance, be careful of the 1% rule. For distance flights less than 100 km, the maximum height loss between start and finish cannot be more than 1% of the distance flown.

For example if you wanted to fly from Lasham to Old Sarum, you would cover 53 kilometres. However Old Sarum is 333 feet lower than Lasham, so your start height should therefore be no more than 530 metres less 333 feet, which works out at just over 1400 feet. If you are not using a flight recorder, this start height will be deemed to be the launch height.

For an aerotow, you will need a certificate from the tug-pilot of the release height and place of release. To ensure that you cover 50km, the place of the release must be on the opposite side of the start line from the direction that you will be travelling. Before you launch, tell the tug-pilot to where you want to be taken. Note the name of the tug-pilot, who will have to sign your launch certificate later.

For a wire launch on a task less than 100km, the flight recorder would be needed to show a launch height that is short of the maximum to comply with the 1% rule.

The 1% rule with a flight recorder

If you have an approved flight recorder, the 1% rule is slightly different. The 1% rule can now be based on the difference in heights between the start and finish zones. After the flight, you can choose any low point in the start zone and any high point in the finish zone. If the highest point in the finish zone is not more than 1% lower, you will not incur a distance penalty. The start and finish zones for this rule are 90° sectors on the side of the start and finish points that are remote from the declared track.

The following conditions apply. If you do not comply with these conditions, the usual 1% rule still applies.

- You must declare the flight by completing a declaration form which then must be witnessed by an official observer.
- You must use an approved flight recorder.
- You must pass through the start and finish zones.
- The point, at which you last cross the start line, is your start point. (The start line is 1km long and runs perpendicularly to the declared track with its middle at the declared start. The finish line is similar.)

For flights over 100km, a similar rule applies, if you have an approved flight recorder. In this case the difference in heights in the start and finish zones must not exceed 1000 metres, otherwise you will incur a distance penalty of 100 times the excess height.

If you use a flight recorder "There must be incontrovertible evidence that the flight recorder was present in the glider" for the flight. This can be done in three ways:
- Ask an OO to seal the flight recorder to the glider any time before take-off. An OO must later break the seal
- An OO makes a pre-flight check of the installation of the flight recorder, notes its number and keeps the glider under continuous observation until it takes off on the claimed flight,
- An OO witnesses the landing and has the glider under continuous observation until the flight recorder installation is checked and flight recorder is put under the watch of the OO while it is downloaded.

Your Silver Distance Flight

Annex C of the Sporting Code provides comprehensive information on the evidence provided by flight recorders.

Pre-flight briefing

You should plan several potential routes in the days before your flight. Before you go to the launch-point, you should get a briefing from an instructor. You should have already reviewed your planned route, and should be aware of the weather, the state of the fields and the NOTAMs.

The instructor should check that you have made adequate preparations and offer a few hints. Be careful of an overload of information at this point. Long before this flight you should have learned all you need to know about the glider, its equipment, navigation, airspace and field landings.

Getting ready to launch

Ensure that all the objects in the cockpit are properly stowed and accessible in flight. (The author once had to land back at the airfield because the drinking water had moved out of reach after the acceleration of a winch-launch.)

Go to the lavatory shortly before take-off. It is easy to forget in the excitement.

You can be easily distracted by the additional complications of flying cross-country for a badge, forgetting some of the basics about flying. If possible, enrol a helper to reduce the fluster when getting ready. Never allow anyone to hurry you at the launch point. Get comfortable, and do your checks as usual.

The flight

The simple priority of tasks is: aviate, navigate and, only if necessary, communicate. Your greatest risk is still collision, and this can occur miles from a gliding site. Your most important task is therefore to look out. This is particularly important in and near thermals.

As you are only flying a relatively short distance, you can afford to soar locally until the lift is reliable and going high. Do not set off unless you are 3000 feet above the ground, and the conditions look good on track. If you set off lower than 3000 feet,

you reduce your chances of finding the next thermal. After all, you are not in a race.

When flying straight, frequently check the bearing shown by your compass. You should also keep a track of where you are on the chart about every 10 minutes to check you position and airspace. Make a note of the time that you pass key landmarks.

If you are high but not climbing well and there is no obvious next thermal, continue on track anyway. A thermal usually appears.

After landing

- Move the glider so that it does not obstruct a landing area
- Secure the glider so that it does not blow over
- Switch off electrical equipment
- Remove valuables
- Contact your home club to tell them that you are safe
- If you have landed in a field, find the land-owner and establish your location
- Arrange retrieve
- Find two people (or one OO) to sign your landing certificate, if you have exceeded 50km.

After getting back

- If you used the method where the flight recorder was sealed to the glider and no OO was present when you landed, an OO will have to unseal the logger from the glider
- Complete the claim form and get it signed by an OO. Send the form with the fee and your gliding certificate to the BGA
- Send a thank-you letter to your farmer, if you landed in a field
- Record your flight in the club's cross-country book
- In later weeks, retrieve other people who have landed out.

FURTHER READING

The purpose of this book is to give essential information to early cross-country pilots. However there are many other books on gliding for pilots at all stages of their careers and for pilots with an interest in more detail. This chapter therefore describes some of the books that are still in print. They have been listed by author alphabetically.

Laws & Rules for Glider Pilots by the BGA

All solo pilots must read *Laws and Rules*. This publication summarises the law as it affects glider pilots and the BGA's regulations and recommended practices. It is available as a download from the BGA.

BGA Instructors' Manual

Despite its exclusive title, this is an informative publication for all pilots and Steve Longland's illustrations are, as usual, excellent. It is available to all pilots from the BGA.

Meteorology and Flight: Pilot's Guide to Weather by Tom Bradbury

Though regarded by many as the definitive book on weather for glider pilots, it is sometimes unclear for the novice.

Pilot's Weather by Brian Cosgrove

This is a clear and useful book, though it is not aimed specifically at glider pilots. It is colourfully illustrated.

Advanced Soaring Made Easy by Bernard Eckey

This is an excellent book on the preparation for cross-country flight and the techniques used in flight. In my opinion it is more useful than Reichmann's book.

The Paths of Soaring Flight by FG Irving

This is a highly technical book covering sailplane design.

Gliding (The British Gliding Association Manual) by Steve Longland

It provides a comprehensive and clear description of aerodynamics and has many good diagrams, though it makes some diversions into history. It contains far more than you must know, but it is made more user-friendly by the highlighting of some of the less important sections by stars.

Gliding: From Passenger to Pilot by Steve Longland

This book is mainly aimed at people who are learning to glide, but nevertheless it has chapters on cross-country, competitions and owning a glider.

The Handbook on Glider Aerobatics by Peter Mallinson and Mike Woollard

This is an excellent book for those strange people who like seeing the world from a new perspective at 3g.

Beginning Gliding by Derek Piggott

Derek Piggott has written books for pilots at all stages and this one is aimed at pilots learning to fly.

Understanding Gliding by Derek Piggott

This book is mainly about aerodynamics, but there are also chapters on the wind and about launching. It is practical and non-technical.

Gliding – A Handbook on Soaring Flight by Derek Piggott

An indication of the success of this book is that it was first published in 1958 and it has been in print ever since with regular updates. Note that it overlaps in several places with his other books, notably Beginning Gliding.

Gliding Safety by Derek Piggott

Despite its title, this book contains an assortment of topics such as how to buy your own glider, aerobatics, instructing, launching, spins and stalls, cloud flying and the use of flaps.

Further reading

Understanding Flying Weather by Derek Piggott

This is a short book that provides some of the basics about weather as it affects glider pilots.

The Private Pilot's Licence Course by Jeremy M Pratt (Airplan Flight Equipment Ltd)

These books are intended for power pilots but, helpfully for glider pilots, you do not need to buy all the volumes to get the relevant information. Volumes 2, 3 and 5 of this book provide a clear and comprehensive description of air law, navigation, meteorology, radio and human factors. It is expensive but meticulous.

Cross Country Soaring by Helmut Reichmann (Airplan Flight Equipment Ltd)

The book is provides some practical advice and much detailed theory about cross-country flying. It contains much material not available elsewhere.

The Glider Pilot's Manual by Ken Stewart

This is not just for pilots who are learning to fly. Many of its chapters including aerodynamics are useful for all pilots. It is modern, clear and well organised.

The Soaring Pilot's Manual by Ken Stewart

This is the companion book to The Glider Pilot's Manual. It is mainly about how to soar and fly cross-country. Among its topics are thermalling, wave, ridges, navigation, landing out, final gliding, ballast and task setting. It is also modern, clear and well organised.

See also:
Sailplane & Gliding (The BGA's bi-monthly magazine)

FAA Glider Flying Handbook

http://www.faa.gov/library/manuals/aircraft/glider_handbook/media/faa-h-8083-13.pdf

Air Navigation Order 2010 CAP393

http://www.caa.co.uk/docs/33/CAP393.pdf

Guide to Visual Flight Rules in the UK

http://www.caa.co.uk/docs/64/VFR_Guide_2011.pdf

Oxygen systems

http://www.bas.uk.net/data2.html

Physiology and gliding

http://amygdala.danlj.org/~danlj/AviationMedicine/index.html

NASA aerodynamics

http://www.grc.nasa.gov/WWW/K-12/airplane/short.html

To save you typing in the links in this book, they (and others) are given on http://www.mccullagh.demon.co.uk/links.htm

ANSWERS

Air law

Q1 What international organisation defines minimum standards for air navigation?

International Civil Aviation Organisation (ICAO)

Q2 Where would you look for a list of temporary hazards that you could encounter today?

Notices to Airmen (NOTAMs) or a Pre-flight Information Bulletin (PIB)

Q3 What publication gives the recommended procedures for aerotowing gliders?

The Laws and Rules for Glider Pilots by the British Gliding Association

Q4 What document contains information about specific aerodromes, dimensions of airspace and other aeronautical services?

Aeronautical Information Publication (AIP)

Q5 What does 'ANO' stand for?

Air Navigation Order (a British statutory instrument)

Airmanship

Q1 You have dropped a bolt and it has disappeared under the seat-pan of your glider. You have declared 300km and cumulus has started to appear. What do you do?

Look for the bolt. Loose objects near the controls are unsafe. Do not fly until you have found it.

Q2 You are flying with a ridge to your left. Another glider is coming the other way. What should you do?

Give way by moving further out to the right

Q3 What mnemonic should be used before aerobatic manoeuvres and for what do the letters stand?

HASSLL Height, Airframe, Straps, Security, Location, Look-out

Q4 What angle does your field of primary vision subtend?

3 degrees

Q5 How should you look out systematically?

Look out by fixing your gaze ahead and then above and below several points on the horizon to your left until you are looking as far behind as possible, then look above and then look ahead again. Check instruments and attitude. Do the same look-out scan to the right. Repeat this cycle as often as possible.

Q6 You are approaching a large town into a headwind at 1000 feet AGL, but you hope to pick up some lift over the town, so that you can get to your home airfield, which is beyond. What should you be thinking about?

You cannot fly over any congested area below 1000 feet above the highest fixed object and within 600 metres. Higher if you cannot land clear.

Q7 What is the minimum height needed to perform aerobatics over a town?

If we assume that the town is a congested area, then there is no minimum height. Aerobatics are <u>not</u> permitted at any height above a congested area.

Q8 You see a powered aircraft coming from your left, what should you do?

In theory you should maintain your course because the other aircraft should avoid you. This assumes that its pilot has seen you. If there is plenty of time, rock the wings to increase your visibility and keep the other aircraft in sight. Only if you see no change of course, take evasive action. The time

Answers

between sighting the other aircraft and taking evasive action is often very short.

Q9 Can a glider fly at less than 500 feet above the ground when it is not taking off or landing?

The aircraft must not fly closer than 500 feet to a person, vessel, vehicle or structure. If none of these objects are present, you can fly below 500feet above flat ground. At that height prudence will usually indicate that you should be about to land. You can also fly lower than 500 feet above the ground when ridge soaring.

Altitude

Q1 You are flying with your altimeter set to QFE above your home airfield which has an elevation of 618 feet AMSL. Above you is Class A airspace that is marked on the chart as 5500′. The sub-scale on your altimeter reads 1002hPa. How high can you fly above the airfield before you infringe the controlled airspace?

4882 feet (5500-618). The airspace here has been defined by an absolute altitude not a flight level which would have been expressed as FL55. The pressure in this case is irrelevant.

Q2 You are climbing towards the lower limit of Class A airspace. What factors might affect your decision about the level at which you will leave the thermal?

Your altimeter is subject to the changing pressure during the day, it may stick unless you tap the panel beside it continuously and you may continue to climb after you straighten up to leave the thermal. If the airspace is defined by a flight level, the sea-level atmospheric pressure will also be a factor.

Q3 You are flying cross-country with your altimeter set to QNH. You are near Compton Abbas airfield which has an ATZ. The airfield is marked on the chart with an elevation of 811 feet. How high AMSL must you be when you fly over the airfield to be clear of its ATZ?

2811 feet AMSL. The ATZ extends 2000 above ground level.

Q4 What settings from your altimeter should you note before you take off to fly cross-country?

You should note the sub-scale setting for QFE and for QNH. Take off on QFE but switch to QNH when you set off.

Q5 You have decided to fly cross-country using QFE. The airfield is at 618 feet and the sub-scale reads 995hPa. What would your altimeter read at the base of FL60?

5454 if you used 1013.2hPa (5460 feet if you used 1013hPa). Sea level pressure is about 618/30 + 995hPa = 1015.6. The base of FL60 is therefore 2.4hPa higher than on a day with the standard sea level pressure of 1013.2hPa. 2.4hPa is equivalent to =72feet (2.4x30). Your altimeter will read 6000 - 618 + 72 = 5454 feet above your airfield. (However you now know that this calculation can be avoided in flight by noting the sub-scale readings before you take off and changing to 1013hPa when you are near airspace defined by a flight level. Change back when you land back at base.

Airspace

Q1 You can comfortably fly above some Class D airspace without infringing it. Is any action needed?

You should still call the controller to tell them that you are above their zone. They may not know your altitude but you will show up on their radar. They may divert traffic around you unless you tell them your altitude.

Q2 How is the class of airspace shown on a half-million-scale chart?

A small oblong contains a capital letter, usually A or D in the area near the name of the airspace.

Q3 What is the maximum size of an ATZ?

Where the longest runway is over 1850 metres, the ATZ extends to a RADIUS of 2.5 nautical miles from the centre of this runway. (For shorter runways, the zone has only a 2 nautical miles radius.)

Q4 How big is a parachute drop zone?
Most are 1.5 nautical miles RADIUS, but they can be 2 nautical miles radius. It is also prudent to stay even further away if upwind.

Q5 What are the two numbers beside high obstacles on a half-million-scale chart?

In bold is the height in feet above sea level. The smaller height is the height above the ground.

Q6   A hatched zone is marked P106/2.5. It is a Sunday. Do you need to call to get permission to cross below 2500 feet altitude?

The P means prohibited. You must never cross a prohibited area (even on a Sunday). There is no crossing service of whom to ask permission.

Q7   You will be flying near an MATZ. What action should you take?

You can fly through a MATZ, though care should be taken. Avoid flying near the extended centre line of the runway.

Q8   You have a close encounter with a light aircraft. What do you do next?

Note the exact time and position and if possible the type and registration of the other party. You should file an Airprox report either immediately if practicable by radio or as soon as you land.

Q9   What does TMA stand for?

A Terminal Manoeuvring Area (or Terminal Control Area) is often established where several routes converge near a major airport. It is usually Class A airspace.

Visibility

Q1   You are flying at 4000 feet altitude in uncontrolled airspace. What is the minimum visibility for you to fly there?

There is no minimum. You can fly in cloud, if you are confident about your abilities to do so.

Q2   What are the risks of flying in cloud?

The greatest risk is of losing control and over-stressing the glider. Because the sky is a large place, there is only a small risk of collision when in the cloud, but radio calls to other glider pilots reduce this. If near mountains, you might also fly into the higher ground.

Q3   You are about to take a wire launch for a brief local flight. The weather was sunny but the sun set only five minutes ago. The canopy is misting up but this will clear shortly after you take-off. What decision should you take about the duration of this flight?

Do not take-off. The misting will not clear in time for a safe launch.

Q4   You decide to call up an ATC unit to cross Class D airspace above 3000 feet AMSL. They ask you to maintain VMC. What visibility do they require you to maintain?

1000 feet below cloud or 1.5 kilometres horizontally from cloud in a flight visibility of 5km

Radio

Q1   You have a 720 channel radio in your glider and a hand-held radio. You do not intend to talk to controllers. Do you need a licence?

You need a licence for both radios but you do not need an FRTOL, provided you do not talk on a frequency of a non-recreational ground station. If the hand-held is only used as a back-up to the glider's radio, only one licence is needed.

Q2   Where do you find the frequency for the ATZ of a parachute drop zone?

The card that accompanies the half million scale map and the NATS Aeronautical Information Service website at http://www.nats-uk.ead-it.com/public/index.php.html

Q3   What is the main purpose of 130.4MHz?

Cloud-flying and cross-country messages

Q4   How would you spell 'chrysanthemum' in the phonetic alphabet?

Charlie, Hotel, Romeo, Yankee, Sierra, Alpha, November, Tango, Hotel, Echo, Mike, Uniform, Mike

Q5   You are asked to 'Read back'. What do you do?

Repeat what you have just been told

Q6   How is an altitude of 1700 feet transmitted?

Wun tousand seven hundred feet

Answers

Q7   How is an altitude of 11,500 feet transmitted?

Wun Wun Tousand fife hundred feet

Q8   If you make a mistake when transmitting, what do you say?

You can either say 'Correction' and then say the last thing you said correctly followed by the right information. Alternatively you could say 'Disregard' meaning that you should consider that the last transmission was not sent.

Q9   What does 'Standby' mean?

Wait and I will call you

Q10   What does a readability of '5' mean?

Perfectly readable

Q11   How would a ground station abbreviate the call-sign 'Glider G-CKDN'?

Glider Delta November

Q12   How is a frequency of 131.025 transmitted?

Wun Tree Wun Dayseemal Zero Two (note the fife is not needed)

Q13   How do you say 'Yes'?

Ay-firm

Q14   How do you say 'No'?

Negative

Q15   If you are told to do something but cannot eg 'maintain height', what do you say?

Unable comply

NOTAMS

Q1   You want the NOTAMs and permanent changes to airspace. Where do you look?

Your club must provide details of permanent changes to airspace and of temporary hazards.   However you can also get NOTAMs by fax, by phone, from the AIS web site and from specialist aviation services on the internet.

Q2   The Red Arrows are performing a display at a village fete on your route. Would you get a good view from your glider?

No. They would cancel the display if you were nearby and the authorities would prosecute.

Q3   You see a NAV warning containing the abbreviation PJE. What does this mean?

PJE means parachute jumping exercise.

Q4   A temporary Class A airway has been established. Under what circumstances can you cross it?

You must not cross the airway between the specified times

Q5 The date and time on a NOTAM was shown as 08/06/05 09:50 What date and time would you infer from this information?

The date is 5th June 2008 and the time is 10:50 British Summer Time.

Navigation

Q1   You decide to fly without drawing your route on your chart.   What difficulties might you encounter?

You will not be able to compare your position with your planned route, you will not have considered the airspace on and near your route, and it will take longer to find your place on the chart each time you pick it up.

Q2   You see a small town that you do not recognise. What can you do to identify it?

Look at the town to see if it has any distinctive features (railways, by-passes, lakes) then look at the chart to see if these features are present on the chart for a town near your planned route and if the relative positions of the features match.

Q3   What must you carry if you fly more than 5 nautical miles from your launch airfield?

A chart clearly marked with the regulated and controlled airspace.

Q4 You are planning a flight to a turning point 100km due north but there is a 10 knot wind coming from 315°. You think your cross country speed without a wind would be 65kph. What true heading should you fly and how long would it take?

Heading 350° true. It should take about 1 hour 51 minutes. 100km at 65kph without any wind takes 1.53 hours, but in that time an 18.5kph wind will blow you 28km. If you draw the line to your turn point, it will be 200mm long. You should now add an additional distance to be overcome because of the wind. Do this by adding a line running northwest from the turn-point. This will be one half millionth of 28km or 56mm. A line from your starting point to the far end of the new line is the resultant from combining the no-wind distance and the additional distance caused by the wind. This line gives you the bearing that you must fly.

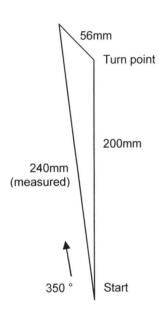

56mm

Turn point

200mm

240mm (measured)

350 °   Start

Q5 You think you may be infringing controlled airspace. What do you do?

If you do not know your position, land. If you know where you are and you can quickly remedy the situation, call up the controller and tell them of your plans.

Landing at another airfield
Q1 On arrival at a strange airfield, you call on the notified frequency but get no reply. Your radio is serviceable, what should your actions be?

Continue with intended landing, watch for other traffic and follow suit and make relevant 'blind calls' on the radio.

(Check the windsock, and if possible look at the signal square.)

Q2 You decide to land beside another aircraft that has just landed. On which side should you pass?

You keep to the right of the other aircraft

Q3 You are circling low near an unknown airfield and you see a red flare. Guy Fawkes' Night is not imminent. Is any action needed?

Do not land on the airfield. The flare is probably directed at you, and you are causing a nuisance if not an offence.

Q4 You see the signal square at an airfield and it contains a large white T. What does this signify?

The T in the signal square shows the direction of landing and take-off along the shaft of the T and towards the cross arm.

Q5 You have identified the airfield of a flying club. You have a radio, and you would like to land there unless you find a thermal. What should you say after establishing contact?

"Glider G-CXYZ is x miles to the north/south/east/west at nnn feet QFE. Request joining information." You should then be told useful information about joining the circuit, altimeter setting, wind and where to land.

Q6 You land at a small airstrip. What should your first action be after stopping?

Push your glider off to the side of the strip

Q7 You want to land at an airfield immediately after a large jet has landed. Where should you land?

The turbulence will be greatest near the touchdown point, so you should land long.

Field landings
Q1 What are the six main factors that should determine your choice of field?

Wind, size, slope, surface, stock and obstructions

Answers

Q2   The normal approach speed of your glider is 55 knots in still air and your landing run is normally 250 metres. You have chosen a flat field that is 700 metres long and you will approach at 60 knots over a 20 metre tree with a 10 knot tail-wind. How far into the field will you stop from the tree?

You would have been stopped by the far boundary hedge 700 metres from the tree. You needed your normal 250 metres plus 200 metres after clearing the 20 metre tree plus 100 metres for your excess speed plus up to 200 metres for the tail wind.

Q3   You decide to land on an up-slope, what effect will this have on your approach speed and round-out?

Your approach speed should be at least 65-70 knots and you should be wary of the optical illusion from up-slopes. Your round-out will be earlier than normal.

Q4   You have a good look at your field from almost above it as you start your downwind leg. What effect may this have on your landing?

Unless you move well away from the field on your downwind leg, you will lose sight of the field sooner, your final turn will be almost 180 degrees and so probably too early and too high.

Q5   At what height above your chosen field would you reject a potential thermal?

800 feet (more, if you would be drifted out of position and so would be unable to follow your intended circuit).

Human factors

Q1   At what height does the law require the use of oxygen?
The Air Navigation Order requires that oxygen be supplied to the flight crew of unpressurised aircraft above FL130 and if above FL100 for more than 30 minutes. (Note that the BGA's Laws and Rules also recommends the use of oxygen above 10,000 feet.)

Q2   What is the approximate time of useful consciousness for an average person at 20,000 feet without supplementary oxygen assuming minimal activity?

Between 5 and 10 minutes.

Q3   You are at 5000 feet and after a scare you feel dizzy, what could be the problem?

You may be hyperventilating.

Q4   You are suffering from a heavy cold which has caused a blocked nose and/or blocked sinuses. Is it safe to fly after taking a decongestant?

No. Decongestants are not completely effective and wear off quickly. Do not fly with a cold.

Q5   As you are descending from a diamond height gain, you experience severe pain in your ears. What should you do?

Perform the Valsalva manoeuvre (close your mouth, pinch your nose and try to blow). If possible reduce your rate of descent.

Q6   During a long cross-country flight, you are feeling drowsy and irritable, what might you do improve the situation?

You may be suffering from dehydration. Consider landing, but otherwise drink more water throughout the rest of the flight. A snack might also help to increase your alertness.

Q7   You have been stowing equipment in your glider and so appear to be slow to get into it. The launch point controller unjustifiably questions your IQ. What might be the effect on your concentration?

You may be under stress and so less able to undertake the imminent launch

Q8   You are 53 but not an instructor, when is your next medical certificate due?

Before your 55th birthday, unless you have had a severe illness.

Principles of flight

Q1   Name the forces on a glider when it is flying straight at a steady speed.

Lift, weight and drag. At a steady speed they balance each other.

Q2   Name the forces on a glider when it is in a well banked turn at a steady speed.

Lift, weight and drag. A proportion of the lift from the wings provides the force needed to change the direction of the glider.

Q3   Why does a glider increase its speed in a turn unless you move the stick back?

Banking the wings means that the lift from the wing is no longer acting vertically, thus reducing the vertical component of the lift. Applying elevator increases the angle of attack and so the wings generate more lift to compensate for the amount of lift lost by banking. If no additional input is made to elevator, the three forces will no longer be in equilibrium. The glider's speed will therefore increase.

Q4   How does profile drag change with air-speed between the stall and V_{NE}?

The profile drag (which includes form drag, skin friction, interference drag, leakage drag and parasitic drag) increases with the square of the speed.

Q5   How does lift-induced drag change with air-speed between the stall and V_{NE}?

Lift-induced drag (which is caused by the meeting of high and low pressure air around the wings) decreases with the square of the speed.

Q6   At what speed is total drag at a minimum?

When total drag is at a minimum, the glider is flying at the speed that gives the best glide angle.

Q7   Why put sealing tape between the wings and fuselage?

The tape reduces interference drag and stops air leaking from the lower wing surface to the upper surface. This leakage causes additional turbulence and reduces the lift generated by the wing.

Q8   Why do you normally apply rudder when applying aileron?

When you bank, the aileron at the up-going wing will generate more lift and so will generate more drag. The large wing-span of a glider provides leverage. This additional drag will therefore yaw the glider in the 'wrong' direction.

Applying rudder provides an opposing yawing force to counter the adverse yaw.

Q9   How can gliders stall at higher speeds?

The air-flow will become turbulent above the wing, if there is a high angle of attack, whatever the air-speed. The wings may already have an increased attack angle, because they are being required to generate more lift. This can arise when the glider is heavier because of ballast, when the glider is turning or pulling g, and when the glider is being winch-launched.

Q10   Why does a glider spin?

A glider spins when there is a high angle of attack and one wing stalls before the other, often because of yaw. The increased drag from the tip of the stalled wing starts the glider rotating.

Q11   What is the purpose of a glider's fin?

It keeps the fuselage pointing in the direction of flight. If the glider yaws right, the air-flow on the left side of the fin will tend to straighten the glider up and so provide directional stability.

Q12   What is the purpose of a tail-plane?

Wings are naturally unstable and will always try to pitch downwards. The tail-plane is therefore used to provide a down-force that tries to raise the nose. When a glider's nose pitches up, the angle of attack of the tail-plane increases, decreasing the down-force that it produces. Conversely, when the nose is lowered, the tail-plane will produce a greater down-force. Consequently the tail-plane resists pitching movement, and is said to provide 'longitudinal stability'.

Q13   How does an elevator work?

The up-force or the down-force generated by the tail-plane can be modified by effectively changing its camber by using the elevator.

Q14   What is the effect on stability of reducing the cockpit load?

The centre of gravity moves back and the glider becomes less stable, ie making it more likely to spin and more difficult to recover.

Answers

Q15 Why is the best glide angle given by the tangent to the polar curve?

A line can be drawn from each point on the polar curve to the origin. The vertical length of this line is vertical speed and the horizontal length of this line is the horizontal speed. In the same length of time, the two lines therefore represent a height lost and a distance travelled ie the glide angle. The slope of the line represents the glide angle. Of all the lines that can be drawn from the curve to the origin, there is only one that only touches the curve at one point (ie the tangent). This line is the one with the least slope (ie best glide angle).

Q16 If you bank a glider, its stall speed increases. Why then is it safer to make a well banked final turn?

Most of the available elevator range has already been used to increase the angle of attack that is compensating for lift that has been lost by banking. The remaining backward movement is insufficient to stall the glider in a steep turn. Backward movement will merely make the turn steeper. In a gentle turn, the stick has not been moved back as far, so there ample of up-elevator still available to increase the angle of attack and stall the glider.

Aircraft structure and integrity

Q1 What name is given to the maximum speed at which it is safe to use full deflection of any one control without damaging the glider?

Maximum manoeuvring speed V_A (which is often set at the same speed as the maximum rough air-speed V_B)

Q2 What is the maximum air-speed and maximum manoeuvring speed of the glider that you normally fly? (You may have to look this up in the flight manual.)

So now you know.

Q3 What is the name given to the certificate that shows the glider has passed its annual inspection?

An Airworthiness Review Certificate (not a Certificate of Airworthiness)

Q4 You were sitting in the cockpit ready to launch when someone drove over your wing-tip. Is this a reportable accident and, if so, to whom?

Since it is after embarkation and it is serious damage, it must be reported as soon as possible to the Police and the Department of Transport Air Accident Investigation Board. It must also be reported to the BGA with 24 hours.

Q5 Your glider's radio is broken. Are you as pilot with a Bronze Badge allowed to take it out and send it for repair?

Yes, if it is under the supervision of an inspector

Instrumentation

Q1 What effect will altitude have on the indicated air-speed?

The indicated air-speed is less than the true air-speed at altitude.

Q2 What do the green and yellow bands on some ASIs mean?

The green band runs from minimum sink speed to the maximum manoeuvring speed and the yellow band runs from the maximum manoeuvring speed to V_{NE}.

Q3 What property of the air is a variometer measuring?

The rate of change of air pressure

Q4 What does a total energy probe do?

It cancels out the changes in altitude caused by changing speed, leaving just the effect from the rising air

Q5 What type of variometer is recommended by the BGA?

Recommended Practice 27 states that "Gliders operating from BGA sites should be equipped with audio variometers and the pilots trained in their use."

Q6 If the Pitot tube is blocked with water or ice, will the ASI over-read or under-read?

The lack of dynamic pressure will cause the ASI to under-read.

Weather

Q1   What does 'Buys-Ballots' Law state for the northern hemisphere?

If you stand with your back to the wind the lower pressure is on your left.

Q2   If a due westerly wind is forecast to veer by 10°, from what direction will it then come?
Veering means the wind direction will change clockwise, so the new direction will be 280°

Q3   How does the wind direction vary as you descend to ground level from 2000 feet?

The wind backs with decreasing altitude. The amount of change depends on the strength of the wind, on whether it is day or night and on the roughness of the surface.

Q4   There is a strong cross-wind. You want to land alongside of and downwind of a row of trees and large hangar, what might happen?

You can expect the wind to be very turbulent downwind of the trees and the hangar. You should expect that wind will suddenly drop as you enter the wind shadow of the hangar and so plenty of extra speed should be used to counter this wind-gradient and sink.

Q5   What causes the wind-speed to increase in the morning and decrease in the evening?

The thermals transport faster moving air downwards making the surface wind stronger and gustier during the day

Q6   What will the effect of a sea-breeze front have on your plans if you have to fly across one?

A sea-breeze front will have a strong line of good lift along its length but on the seaward side there will be more stable air and so fewer, if any, thermals.

Q7   What effect will the passage of a sea-breeze front have had if you make a field landing?

The passage of a sea-breeze front can cause the wind direction to change by up to 180° and to increase by up to 20 knots. Any landing (and landing in a small field in particular) will be hazardous unless the change in direction and speed has been noticed.

Q8   What is the dew point?

The dew point is the temperature at which a body of air becomes saturated, ie holds the maximum amount of water vapour.

Q9   What are the environmental lapse-rate, the dry adiabatic lapse-rate and the saturated lapse-rate?
The environmental lapse-rate is the rate at which temperature of the air in general changes with height. The dry adiabatic lapse-rate applies to a parcel of dry air that has been heated by the ground. This parcel will cool at about 3°C for every 1000 feet. The saturated lapse-rate is the rate at which the air will cool when its water starts condensing. The condensation releases latent heat so the saturated lapse-rate is only 1.5°C for every 1000 feet at low level.

Q10   The maximum temperature is forecast to be 22 °C and the dew point is 7 °C. Roughly how high will the cumulus cloud-base be?

A wide spread between the surface temperate and the dew point implies a high cloud base. Take the difference between air temperature and dew point and multiply by 400 to get the cloud-base in feet. For example if the surface temperature is 22°C and the dew point 7°C the difference is 15, which puts the cloud-base at about 6000ft. (15 x 400). However this is subject to inversions, so the thermals may never get this high.

Q11   You are ridge soaring and find that cloud is forming over the hill. What is the type of cloud called?

Orographic cloud

Q12   In the summer, what is often the first sign of an approaching warm front?
The first sign of an approaching warm front is a high layer of cirrus and then cirro-stratus which will begin to cut off the thermals.

Q13   You are landing your glider near a thunderstorm, what is your greatest risk?

Answers

You should expect strong gusts of wind from unexpected directions and possibly strong sink, so that landing will be difficult.

Q14 What is the cause of radiation fog?

At night, the ground loses heat to space by radiation. The air near the ground is cooled by the ground and if the air is moist and there is little wind, the moisture condenses giving rise to a low level layer of fog, or perhaps just pockets of fog in low-lying moist areas.

Q15 What would be the effect on thermals of an inversion layer in an anticyclone in the summer?

The air will rise until it reaches the inversion and will rise no further. If the air has not cooled to the dew point by the time that it has reached the inversion layer, no clouds will form and it will therefore be 'blue'. If the air is moist, the clouds could form and spread out at the inversion layer.

Q16 You notice that the cumulus clouds are rising to great heights above their bases and flattening at their tops. What could happen next?

Thunderstorms are likely and you should consider landing instead of going in their direction.

Q17 It is July and the weather feels fresh. A ridge of high pressure is forecast. What weather would you expect?

It should be great weather but there are no guarantees. Even so, tell your boss that you want to take the next day as vacation.

Q18 There has been a shower while your glider has been at the front of the winch-launch queue but flying is about to restart. What should you do?

Dry off the whole glider.

Q19 You are on a gliding holiday in the Pyrenees and because thunderstorms are forecast, you decide not to fly that day. Should you de-rig the glider?

The closer to the equator you go, the more powerful the thunderstorms, especially in the mountains. Rarely, but

sufficiently often to worry local farmers, storms produce massive hailstones that will wreck the delicate surfaces of gliders and sometimes even cars. There will also be high winds in the squalls that are associated with a thunderstorm and there is a risk of the heavy rain penetrating vents. De-rig.

Q20 What might you experience near a rotor cloud?

Downwind of a mountain you can expect considerable turbulence and this is often associated with a rotating cloud known as a rotor cloud. Just above the rotor you might find wave.

Q21 In which direction would the wind tend to blow in the mountains in high summer during the afternoon?

As the thermals begin in the mountains, air is drawn along the valleys to replace the rising air.

Use and care of parachutes

Q1 In addition to thinking about launch failures, what else should you include in the eventualities part of your pre-flight checks?

Think about which straps you would undo to bale out and where the canopy jettison knob is. Work out whether you have to pull the canopy release knob and the jettison knob.

Q2 You collide with another glider but your own glider seems OK. What should you do?

If you stay with the glider, you might be lucky, but you might not be. Baling out is the safe option.

Q3 You are descending on a parachute. The ground is rushing up fast, what should be your body position?

Keep your feet and knees together and bend your knees. Put your chin on your chest, clench your teeth, hunch your shoulders and hold the webbing high up in each hand. Keep your elbows in. The trick is not to face fully forward or backwards to your direction of travel but the land side on. Crumple as you land to dissipate the energy.

CONVERSION FACTORS

From	To	Multiply by
Metres	Feet	3.281
Feet	Metres	0.3048
Millimetres	Inches	0.0394
Inches	Millimetres	25.40
Kilometres	Miles	0.6214
Miles	Kilometres	1.609
Kilometres	Nautical Miles	0.5396
Nautical Miles	Kilometres	1.853
Nautical miles	Feet	6080
Kilometres per hour	Miles per hour	0.6214
Miles per hour	Kilometres per hour	1.609
Kilometres per hour	Knots	0.5396
Knots	Kilometres	1.85
Miles per hour	Knots	0.869
Knots	Miles per hour	1.151
Feet per minute	Metres per second	0.005084
Metres per second	Feet per minute	196.85
Knots	Metres per second	0.515
Metres per second	Knots	1.944
Square metres	Square feet	10.764
Square feet	Square metres	0.093
Kilograms	Pounds	2.205
Pounds	Kilograms	0.454
Inches of mercury	Millibars	33.8
Millimetres of mercury	Millibars	1.33

To convert Fahrenheit to Celsius, subtract 32, divide by 9 and multiply by 5
To convert Celsius to Fahrenheit, divide by 5, multiply by 9 and add 32

INDEX

Index

Index